Wonders of
the Modern World

Books by Joseph Gies

Wonders of the Modern World
Bridges and Men
*Adventure Underground: The Story of the World's
    Great Tunnels*

Wonders of the Modern World

BY JOSEPH GIES

Thomas Y. Crowell Company
NEW YORK
Established 1834

Designed by Nancy Dale

Manufactured in the United States of America

Library of Congress Catalog Card No. 66-14488

Second Printing, November 1966

Some of the illustrations in chapter 11 have been adapted from
American Telephone and Telegraph publications and are
used by permission.

Contents

Illustrations

Photographs (*following page 114*)

Drawings

Foreword

THE IDEA of compiling a list of wonders of the world is
not original with this writer. Twenty-two hundred years ago
Antipater of Sidon named the Pyramids of Egypt, the
Hanging Gardens of Babylon, the giant statue of Zeus at
Olympia, the Temple of Diana at Ephesus, the Mausoleum
at Halicarnassus, the Colossus of Rhodes, and the lighthouse on the island of Pharos near Alexandria as the seven
outstanding works to have come from the hand of man.
With the exception of the Alexandrian lighthouse, built by
the practical-minded Macedonian Greeks, the ancient wonders were all spectacularly nonutilitarian. The kings and
priests had the money to build wonders, and their taste
ran to tombs, temples, and statues.

As Antipater's nominations reflect the values of his day,
the wonders cited in this book reflect our own—our belief
in man's mission to conquer nature, to overcome the physi-
cal universe. From the technical rather than social view-
point, these modern works are not so different from those
of Antipater. Engineers employing a combination of theoretical knowledge, practical experience, and improvisation
built the Pyramids, just as today they are building the
Aswan Dam in the same country. If Antipater's wonders
are characterized by a high degree of aesthetically pleas-

ing content, today's construction jobs are by no means aesthetically empty. In 1964, the Museum of Modern Art in New York exhibited enlarged photographs of 195 engineering works; the enthusiastic captions for the photos might have led an observer to conclude that dams, oil refineries, factories, powerhouses, and highway overpasses are created for no other purpose than to express their builders' artistic impulses.

The real why and how of engineering is often an intricate story. To learn it, a writer needs considerable assistance from engineers, who luckily are a very helpful group of men. This writer's sincere thanks are due to the American Society of Civil Engineers (A.S.C.E.), and in particular to William H. Wisely, Executive Secretary, and Herbert Hands, manager of the A.S.C.E. Public Information Office. A.S.C.E. members made helpful suggestions and corrections on almost every chapter. But apologies are also owed to engineers and to engineering amateurs for the omission from this book of many achievements that deserve to be in it. During 1952, the A.S.C.E.'s centennial year, the Society undertook an exhaustive study and poll of its members to pick the "Seven Modern Civil Engineering Wonders in the United States." The debate that developed held up final selection till 1955, when the chairman of the committee, Dr. James Kip Finch, described the seven that were chosen in *Civil Engineering* magazine: the Chicago sewage system, Colorado Aqueduct, the Empire State Building, the Grand Coulee Dam and Columbia Basin Project, Hoover Dam, the Panama Canal, and the San Francisco–Oakland Bay Bridge. In the decade since, engineers, architects, and scientists have contrived many marvels: satellites, jetports, TV towers, nuclear reactors,

domed baseball parks. Several of these were omitted with
real regret—the beautiful Chesapeake Bay Bridge–Tunnel, for one. Some of the works omitted from the text are
partially dealt with in the appendixes.

I wish to cite the following for special assistance:

The American Bridge Division of United States Steel;
the Triborough Bridge and Tunnel Authority; the Bethlehem Steel Company; "Verrazano-Narrows Bridge,"
symposium, *Civil Engineering*, Hal Hunt, Editor; "The
Bridge," by Gay Talese; "The Narrows Bridge at New
York," by O. H. Ammann; "Planning and Design of the
Narrows Bridge," by O. H. Ammann; Ammann & Whitney, New York.

Japanese National Railways, Mr. Fachio Nakanishi, Director; Railway Age; *International Railway Journal*.

Les grands tunnels des Alpes et du Jura, by James La-
dame Dubuisson; *Problemes du projet et de l'establisse-
ment de grands souterrains routiers alpins*, by Charles
Andreae; *Tunnels*, by Gosta Sandstrom; *Vom Bau des
Simplontunnels*, by Paul Attinger.

Ray Josephs Public Relations Ltd., Empire State Building archives; "The Origin of the Skyscraper," report of
a committee appointed by the Estate of Marshall Field;
"Wind Forces on a Tall Building," by J. Charles Rathbun.

The Atomic Energy Commission, Mr. Watson Feni-
more; the Society of Naval Architects and Marine Engineers, Captain W. N. Landers, United States Navy; University of Michigan Phoenix Project.

The Bureau of Public Roads, Rex M. Whitton, Federal
Highway Administrator; the American Road Builders' As-
sociation, Mr. Randolph T. Russell; *The Saturday Evening
Post*.

The Metropolitan Sanitary District of Greater Chicago, especially former Chief Engineer Norval Anderson, General Superintendent Vinton W. Bacon, and Ben Sosewitz. The Department of Water Resources of California, Mr. William E. Warne, Director; *Western Construction*, Mr. Bob Byrne, Editor.

The Ministry of Sadd-el-Aali of the United Arab Republic; the Information Service of the United Arab Republic; the *Unesco Courier*; Rex Keating of Unesco; Vattenbyggnadsbyran of Stockholm.

The Netherlands Information Service, Mr. Fen Damen; *The Engineer*, of London; "Holland and the Delta Plan," by J. F. Lingsma.

Public Information Division of American Telephone and Telegraph, Miss Nadine Golladay; Bell Telephone Laboratories and *Bell Laboratories Record; Bell Telephone Magazine*; Comsat.

The Strategic Air Command; Daniel, Mann, Johnson and Mendenhall; *Aerospace Engineering; This Week; Popular Science; Fortune.*

The Northeast Public Relations Office of the Ford Motor Company, Mr. John Cameron; the General Electric Company; the Bunker-Ramo Corporation; "Automation," by the American Assembly; "The Anatomy of Automation," by Amber and Amber.

The above is by no means a complete list of sources. One source that made valuable contributions to several chapters is *The Engineering News-Record*, inheritor and able upholder of a fine tradition of technical writing and editing.

Wonders of
the Modern World

1
Something New on the Sea:
N.S. *Savannah*

GOING ABOARD the N.S. *Savannah,* as many thousands of American and foreign visitors have discovered, is very different from going aboard an ordinary ship. You not only are permitted to wander through the whole ship, you are taken on a guided tour. Its mission is to show as many people as possible the potential of nuclear power for navigation.

In the course of your tour, you pass through the dining room. Here you see a model ship that explains why the *Savannah,* which was launched in Camden, New Jersey, got its name. It is because of an odd thing that happened one warm spring day in 1819 in the Irish Channel. That morning a small vessel in evident distress was sighted. Black smoke was pouring out of her hull. The officer of the day in the port of Cork notified the admiral; the admiral ordered out the cutter, which, under full sail, soon drew alongside the stricken foreigner. At close range, it suddenly became apparent that the stranger, the American packet *Savannah,* was in no need of aid. The smoke was rising from a black chimney located between her mainmast and foremast. Midships on either side, she carried a housing under which a big paddlewheel turned.

For the first time, a steamship had crossed the Atlantic. She had not, it is true, crossed entirely, or even mainly, on steam; for though she carried neither cargo nor passengers and her little 300-ton hull was entirely crammed with fuel, the pine logs burned so swiftly that her boilers were good for only 89 hours out of a 24-day crossing. All the rest of the time, her spread of square canvas, carried on three masts, and her triangular jibs bore her along. She was a regular sailing ship with a small steam engine and removable paddlewheels added. She set no records for speed or for anything else. Yet she introduced the greatest revolution in maritime history.

George Fitch, John Stevens, John Rennie, Robert Fulton, and others had proved that James Watt's steam engine could be made to push a boat through water. Several such craft were already chuffing up and down the Ohio and Mississippi. The mission of the first *Savannah*, built by Crocker and Fickett at Corlears Hook, New York, was to prove the practicability of steam for ocean navigation. Despite a reliance on sails for most of the voyage from her Savannah, Georgia, home port to Liverpool, she did the job she set out to do. As soon as the breeze died, her skipper, Captain Moses Rogers, rang the engine room; the fire was kindled; wood was piled on; the water began to boil; and soon the retractable paddlewheels were turning in the water. The *Savannah* slapped through the gentle swells at 7 knots, astonishing an occasional fishing boat and stirring the envy of becalmed schooners. As soon as the wind came up, the fire was doused; enough pine fuel was saved on the crossing to surprise the British cutter in the Irish Channel.

Maritime circles were not greatly impressed by this performance, reasoning that a ship entirely loaded with fuel cannot be a very profitable proposition. However, though it was not immediately clear, the truth was that all the *Savannah* needed was a bit of perfecting to put an end to the three-thousand-year-old Age of Sail. What was even less clear—few people are aware of it even today—was that the new Age of Steam was going to be short in comparison with its predecessor.

It soon became apparent that the true basis of steam navigation on the ocean was fossil fuel—first coal, later oil. Twenty years after the *Savannah*'s crossing, the British H.M.S. *Sirius* accomplished the westward crossing against the prevailing winds under steam power alone. She barely made it, her stubborn skipper refusing to hoist sails even though the coal ran out. Feeding spars into the furnace and holding off a crew threatening to mutiny, he sighted Sandy Hook, New Jersey, just in time.

On July 21, 1959, the first successor to the vast brood of coal-and-oil-powered offspring of the original *Savannah* was launched at Camden, New Jersey. What was strange about the appearance of *Savannah* II was the disappearance of the smokestack, which had been the most startling feature of *Savannah* I. In its place, a little astern of amidships, rises an unobtrusive deck in front of the bridge with an oddly large, square hatch cover. This hatch cover is not designed to be lifted often. Underneath it is a well-secured steel dome. When this is removed, twenty-one round metallic circles come into view. These are the tops of twenty-one rods that control the nuclear "fire" surrounding them.

A nuclear-powered reactor produces heat, which can be used in a variety of ways. Instead of coal, it "burns" a fissionable substance, usually a special form of the heavy-metal uranium, which is composed of atoms that can easily be split in two. As these fly apart at great speed, they generate heat by colliding with surrounding matter. At the same time, neutron particles are released from the centers of the splitting atoms. These may strike other atoms, causing further fission, and so keep the chain reaction going. The heat given off is picked up by a coolant, usually water, which in the process generates steam that is used in the ordinary way to turn turbines.

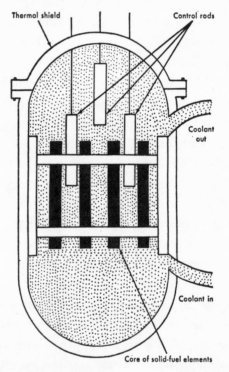

Power unlimited: Simplified diagram of a pressurized-water nuclear reactor. Reaction begins when control rods (white) are entirely withdrawn.

The *Savannah's* reactor consists of five principal elements:

1. *The core.* This contains the fuel, 682,000 thimble-sized pellets of uranium oxide, packed in tubes that are arranged in bundles, weighing a total of 17,000 pounds, and supplying fuel to run the ship 300,000 nautical miles at 20 knots.

2. *The control rods.* These are long cylinders of boron steel that reach down into the core. There are two separate sets—one for regular operation, the other for emergency control. Withdrawing or inserting these rods controls the reaction, because the boron then absorbs more or fewer of the neutrons that cause atom splitting.

3. *The coolant,* or *heat-removal system.* Ideally, from the point of view of efficiency, a single coolant is used, circulating around the hot core and out to wherever it is given off. In the *Savannah's* reactor, as in those of nuclear submarines, two separate systems of water are circulated —the *primary* and the *secondary.* The primary water is under pressure, 1,735 pounds per square inch, which pre-vents it from turning to steam even at an operating temper-ature of around 500 degrees Fahrenheit. A *heat exchanger* transfers heat from the pressurized primary water to the unpressurized secondary water, which promptly changes to steam. This steam turns the turbines and then passes on to a chamber where it is cooled by sea water and returns to repeat its cycle.

4. *The primary shield.* The part of the fission energy that does not appear as heat appears instead as radiation (beta and gamma rays). To keep these lethal particles from escaping, a 17-foot-high lead-covered steel doughnut with 33 inches of water between the two walls surrounds the reactor vessel. The fuel core is only 60 inches high; so the 17-foot tank, whose lead overcoat is thickest opposite

the core, overlaps it top and bottom by a large margin. It keeps the escaping radiation down low enough (200 microroentgens per hour 30 minutes after shutdown) so that workmen can come close for inspection and maintenance.

5. *The secondary shield.* This is the containment vessel itself—the whole globular external cover that encloses the reactor and primary coolant system. Roughly cylindrical in shape, 50.5 by 35 feet in diameter, it is a steel shell resting in a cradle of 4-foot-thick concrete. The top half is covered by a 6-inch layer of lead plus 6 inches of polyethylene plastic. It is there for one reason only—in case of a major operating accident—but every precaution has been taken to make sure that no such accident occurs. Heavy collision bulkheads and collision mats of steel and timber were built into the midsection of the ship. If a major accident should occur because of a collision, storm, enemy action, or some unforeseeable trouble, the containment vessel would check the escape of massive radiation. It would also help protect the reactor from damage.

The shielding conceals the reactor itself from view as one descends below deck, but the general layout of the operating section of the ship is revealed to the line of visitors who crowd the observation gangway overlooking the reactor control room.

Astern of the reactor and its coolant system, outside the containment vessel, can be seen the two big turbines, the main features of the machinery hold that occupies the full width of the ship's beam. They are driven by the steam produced by the secondary water, and, in turn, ultimately drive the propeller shaft.

Behind the turbines lies the nerve center of the ship. A specially designed glass panel has been installed to allow visitors to look in. What they see is an enormous console with dozens of dials that is under the supervision of the engineers on duty (in port, a standby crew only).

The *Savannah's* full complement includes fifteen engineers as well as a water chemist and a team of nuclear instrumentation technicians. The ship's officers report that she handles exceptionally well. The response of the reactor to a demand for a change in speed is two to four times as fast as that of a conventional power source. This provides easy maneuverability. Of course, what the men in the control room spend most of their time doing is not actually operating the ship, but monitoring its intricate systems by keeping a check on the many dials that indicate current oil pressure, water pressure, steam pressure, speed of coolant flow, and potential leaks.

On leaving the reactor control room, one passes into a very fine, modern, but quite ordinary, ship. Built to carry sixty passengers as well as 9,400 tons of cargo, the *Savannah* is excellently, if not luxuriously, appointed. The ship has a sun deck with swimming pool and a commodious dining room. Handsome in a trim way, from the outside the ship presents a gracefully sculptured silhouette. The *Savannah* is 595.5 feet over-all from bow to stern, with a beam of 78 feet and a draft of 29.5 feet, and a displacement of 22,000 tons. Her cruising speed is 21 knots, though she can do better. Passengers sailed to Europe aboard her during demonstration trips in 1964 for a passage fee of $265 to $350. A shorter trip—from New York to Providence was one—cost as little as $40. In 1965, the *Savannah* was licensed for regular commercial operation —another significant first.

When President Eisenhower originally proposed building the world's first nuclear-powered merchant vessel in 1955, there was a certain amount of carping over the cost, which Congress nonetheless authorized. The pioneer ship was designed by George G. Sharp, Inc., New York, and was launched at the yards of the New York Shipbuilding Corporation in Camden, on July 21, 1959. Through 1960, 1961, and into 1962, an elaborate test program was carried out. First, all the components and systems were individually tested. Then the reactor was loaded with its fuel elements and tested with "zero power." Next, it was run with power applied up to 10 percent, and then power up to 100 percent was used. During this phase, the *Savannah* was taken to sea from Yorktown, Virginia, where she had been moved. The ship had no trouble exceeding her designed 20-knot cruising speed, and despite several minor problems she operated efficiently. One fairly sizable problem developed, chronic leakage in the hydraulic system, and before the full-power tests were run, the precaution was taken of reducing the oxygen content inside the containment vessel to below 10 percent to eliminate any fire hazard.

In August 1962, the *Savannah* sailed on her maiden voyage from the test port of Yorktown to her home port of Savannah. From there, she sailed to Norfolk, Virginia, then back south and through the Panama Canal to the West Coast and Hawaii. In early 1963, she entered the nuclear servicing pier specially built for her at Galveston, Texas. Complicated labor problems arose that kept her from sea until a new general agent, American Export Isbrandtsen Lines, was appointed and a new crew trained. In the spring of 1964, she visited Gulf and Eastern ports and in the summer made a series of European crossings.

There can be no doubt that the total cost of the *Savan-*

nah's program, about $80 million, has been well worth it. She has fulfilled both her functions—providing the indispensable practical basis for the development of nuclear-propulsion technology and giving the general public a visible demonstration of the value and safety of the new type of power.

This brings us to the question: How safe is she? To appreciate the completeness of the protective measures taken by the *Savannah's* design engineers, one must realize first of all exactly what the danger is. The fuel in the reactor cannot explode like an atomic bomb. In the case of a major reactor failure, the elements will simply melt, producing terrific heat and—this is the danger—loosing a terrific volume of radiation.

To cope with the danger, nuclear scientists and engineers have approached it from two different directions. First, there is *shielding;* second, there is *scram.*

The shielding begins with the original fuel elements themselves. The fuel pellets are sealed in *cladding tubes* of stainless steel, with the inert gas helium filling the crevices. Cladding not only protects the fuel from corrosion and erosion by the water coolant but locks in the radioactive fission products formed as the fuel atoms undergo fission. Thus, cladding is the first-line radiation shield. A number of cladding tubes clustered together are placed in a rectangular zirconium-alloy enclosure equipped with end fittings that permit the coolant to enter and leave. This assembly is the *fuel element,* and its enclosures form the second line of radiation defense. Several hundred such elements are held in place by grid plates in the reactor core, which is surrounded by the thermal and biological shields. Outside these is the massive containment vessel itself, holding the reactor, the heat exchanger, the pressurizer, the steel drums, and related valves and piping.

All this constitutes the shield defense. But accident prevention being far preferable to accident cure in nuclear engineering as in any other kind, the *Savannah* designers have put their greatest effort into an elaborate and highly sophisticated fail-safe system. The basis of control in a reactor lies in the fact that while 99 percent of the neutrons released by atom splitting fly out instantaneously, a few neutrons are thrown off by fission fragments after a short delay of about 10 seconds. This delay is what makes possible mechanical control of the chain reaction, which takes place when the fission process produces enough particles so that some of them strike other atoms and create more fission. Only a very small number of the particles released actually do strike other atoms. This total number can be kept within the margin of 1 percent. Thus, some of the delayed particles are needed to keep the reaction going. If anything goes wrong—if the process starts moving too fast or too slow, these delayed particles insure that the change happens slowly enough for the control mechanisms to react.

The boron-steel control rods that reach down into the core are operated in two sets. One set, the *control,* or *safety, rods,* form a mechanical unit. When in place, they completely inhibit the chain reaction by soaking up the stray neutrons. The control rods fall into place by gravity and only remain withdrawn when they are so commanded. While they are in the withdrawn position, they are subject to being triggered for falling into place by a whole set of automatic and manual commands. If temperature somewhere rises a few degrees too high, they fall into place. If a hydraulic leak is detected, they fall. If something goes wrong with the electrical system, they fall. If an operator pushes the wrong button, they fall. During the trials and early runs of the *Savannah's* first year they fell into place thirty-five times, usually while the ship was in dock, and most often because of electrical static in the instrument system. This fall of the control rods into place is the *scram*. Scram can also be initiated manually.

Even when the safety rods are withdrawn, no chain reaction is possible until some of the operating rods are also withdrawn. This is done in a programmed sequence. The electrically operated rod-drive mechanisms are backed up by emergency systems powered by nickel-cadmium and lead-acid batteries, enclosed in watertight compartments.

What if the ship turns over? Would the rods fall out and release the radiation? This has been thought of. If the ship's attitude exceeds 45 degrees from the vertical, a gyroscopic-activated capsize switch automatically scrams all twenty-one rods.

The control system was summed up by an engineer friend of mine who worked on some of the components. "They've got back-ups on top of back-ups," he said. "I wish airplanes—automobiles—I wish my wife's kitchen was that safe."

Furthermore, in the restrained language engineers use when speaking on the record, future nuclear propulsion systems will be "superior to that of the *Savannah*," according to the five authors of "NS *Savannah* Operating Experience," a paper presented before the Society of Naval Architects and Marine Engineers.

When one recalls the boiler explosions that maimed and killed crewmen and drowned passengers in the early steamboat days, the safety record of nuclear reactors in general (there are several hundred operating in the United States alone) is reassuring evidence that at least in some ways the twentieth century is more cautious than the nineteenth.

The *Savannah* was not of course the first nuclear ship. In the United States, a fleet of nuclear-powered submarines preceded it, while a frigate, a missile cruiser, and an aircraft carrier have been built along with the *Savannah*. In the Soviet Union, how many submarines or surface ships are powered by reactors is unknown, but the 16,000-ton icebreaker *Lenin* was described as early as 1961. The significant point about all these ships is that they were not designed to earn their way. They are subsidized, special-purpose vessels. Yet the nuclear ship has a tremendous built-in advantage over her old-fashioned rivals—she can run practically indefinitely without ever refueling.

Once the reactor cost drops just a few percentage points, the *Savannah's* daughters will chase the smokestacks from the seven seas. When the technological and commercial conditions of 1819 are compared with those of the 1960's, it is evident that the second *Savannah* enjoys a distinct advantage over the first. For the original *Savannah* to compete effectively with the clipper ships, two fundamental improvements were needed—coal fuel and the screw propeller. Today, nuclear propulsion needs only some very modest advances that are already discernible on the horizon. Capital costs of new reactor systems have been more than halved since the *Savannah's* reactor was installed. Fuel-cycle costs also have been sharply reduced. Nuclear power for marine propulsion is already near the break-even point. Lessons learned from the *Savannah's* operation have led to the design of much more compact reactors, saving still more cargo space. These smaller reactors are more powerful, further increasing capacity for sustained high cruising speeds and prolonged uninterrupted operation, the two basic present advantages of nuclear propulsion.

In its report to the Maritime Administration, the George G. Sharp company, designers of the *Savannah*, predicted that a fleet of fast nuclear freighters could create a new kind of marine transportation in the immediate future. The report estimated that a fleet of 30-knot freighters big enough for express service on a North Atlantic route would cost less to operate than the same number of conventional ships. There is a growing demand for high-speed bulk-cargo carriers for a variety of consumer goods and other freight. An important part of the *Savannah's* mission has been to clear away the legal and insurance obstacles to nuclear-ship acceptance. The solution of these international red-tape problems and the solution to cheaper nuclear power have been running neck and neck. Now commercial nuclear ships—refrigerated cargo carriers, passenger liners, freighters, icebreakers, even a merchant submarine —are being planned in countries around the world.

2
The Fastest Railroad:
The Tokaido Line

CERTAIN TECHNOLOGICAL DEVELOPMENTS prove so wonderfully serviceable that the whole area in need of them is crammed to saturation with the very first models, and there is no room for making badly needed improvements. Such has been the unhappy fate of the railroad, certainly one of the most successful pieces of technology ever to come along. The first railroad, built in England to carry coal from Edward Pease's Darlington mines to the port of Stockton, 8 miles distant, was originally designed as a horse-drawn operation. When George Stephenson, a bright young mine mechanic with a thick North Country accent, told Pease he would be crazy to use horses to pull single coal wagons when he could instead use Stephenson's steam engine to pull a whole string of wagons, neither had any idea of what they were starting. The iron rails spread with lightning rapidity all over England and all over the world. Roadbeds were compacted too hastily, bridges thrown up before materials or designs were good enough, tunnels driven and lined for only single-track operation. A few decades of frenzied building, and suddenly every country had a complete network of railroads with bridges falling down, roadways washing out, trains jumping tracks, and various other mishaps chronic to the system. The steel-truss bridge, steel rails, better roadbeds, and better switching and signaling equipment gradually improved railroad safety and efficiency, but in some ways, the damage had been done. A railroad line conjured up farms and villages and turned bush-league towns into big cities. Second guesses on station sites and on double tracking became very expensive. Curves and grades that could be eliminated thanks to improved tunneling had to be left because the new right of way could not be acquired. Heavily metropolitan stretches with dozens of important stops defied railroad planners to improve service. How could twenty or thirty more fast expresses that were badly needed to handle increased passenger loads be crowded onto the tracks of a solid metropolitan belt like that stretching from Boston to Washington? Or from Tokyo to Osaka?

It almost could not be done, and many people said it was impossible, but the Japanese National Railways undertook to do it for the Tokyo-Osaka stretch, and what they accomplished may well spell the future for the even bigger Boston-Washington metropolitan corridor, not to mention several other places in the world in the next half century.

Along 300 miles of the east coast of Honshu live forty million people, surrounded by two thirds of the industry of Japan. Today, through this belt of people, houses, factories, cities, suburbs, and occasional bursts of countryside, streak the blue-and-white bullets of the New Tokaido Line at speeds of 125 mph. This all new, scientifically designed, and painstakingly constructed railroad line is convincing proof that railroads aren't dead. It also is a beautiful dramatization of the problem—one that government and business generally, not just the railroads, must face.

Japan's rapid industrialization of a hundred years ago centered in the Tokyo-Osaka regions, always politically and commercially important. Inevitably, traffic between the two cities was heavy, but the journey by horseback took nearly a month. The obvious answer was a railroad line, and Japan's first, from Tokyo to Osaka along the Tokaido River, was laid in 1872. Stations were built in most of the towns and villages along the way, and many soon grew into large cities. Today Nagoya is a metropolis of nearly two million inhabitants; Osaka, over three million; and Tokyo, the largest city in the world, with nearly nine million.

By the mid-twentieth century the old Tokaido Line, though representing only 3 percent of the total mileage of Japanese railroad tracks, was carrying one fourth of the freight. Furthermore, the rate of passenger and freight traffic combined was increasing at better than 6 percent a year.

Everything that could be done to improve efficiency on the old line had been done—electrification, color-light signaling, automatic cab signaling, and automatic coupling. Between 240 and 260 trains were operating per day; the line was at saturation point. Despite a great increase in motor transport, the demand for more railroad capacity was imperative.

The Japanese National Railways, a wholly government-owned corporation, began an intensive study in the late 1950's. The most obvious solution was to add two more tracks to the existing Tokaido Line. This was neither simple nor cheap. The old line passed through the very heart of the biggest industrial districts, where land was at a premium. The country it traversed was rugged, with many streams and dozens of major bridges and tunnels that would have to be replaced or widened. Veterans among the railroad's engineers still remembered the appalling struggle they had had with the Tanna Tunnel, the key element in a cutoff on the Izu Peninsula. Tunneling is a far more efficient science today, and one in which Japanese engineers are outstanding, but for this very reason the old line offered a marked disadvantage. Its creators had given it numerous windings and turnings specifically designed to avoid bridging and tunneling. Consequently, the old roadway is not well suited to high-speed operation.

What was needed, the engineers decided, was an entirely new line, which would take over the high-speed operations, both passenger and freight. Two important advantages of this plan were stated by Hideo Shima, chief engineer of the Japanese National Railways:

> It would not be possible otherwise to eliminate all level crossings with road and other railways. . . . Also, the separation of fast and slow trains by tracks will even out the speed of trains on each track, making it possible to raise the capacity of all tracks through more equitable operation of trains, with smaller intervals between them.

Should the old and new lines be given interior connections to enable trains to pass at main stations from one line to the other? The question was carefully weighed, and finally answered in the negative. The expense involved in remodeling stations and yards would have been tremendous, and some of the advantages of superhigh-speed operation sacrificed. Instead, plans were made for facilities in the major centers for easy transfer of passengers and freight from the new stations to the old.

Thus, Shima and his colleagues were able to plan a line in complete freedom from the restrictions that revising the old line, or even connecting with it, would have imposed. This decision for freedom—the determination to take the loss and build from scratch—is the great single lesson of the New Tokaido. Its first fruit was the adoption of the Western standard (4 foot 8 inch) gauge in place of the old narrow (3 foot 6 inch) gauge of all other Japanese railroads. This wider gauge not only provides bigger, more economical passenger and freight cars but is much safer at high speeds.

And speed was the heart of the New Tokaido planning. Stations were limited to ten between Tokyo and Osaka terminals (from Tokyo west: Yokohama, Odawara, Atami,

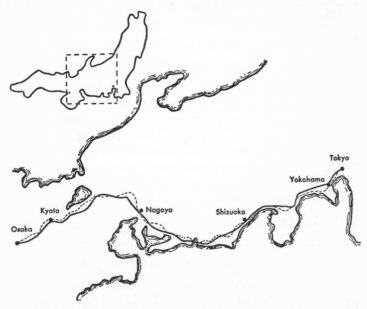

Solid line shows the New Tokaido R.R., which follows a much straighter route than the old line (dotted line). Inset shows the section of Honshu, Japan, that is served by the railroad.

Shizuoka, Hamamatsu, Toyohashi, Nagoya, Hajima, Maibara, and Kyoto). The line was surveyed and laid out for maximum straightaway, minimum grades, and minimum curves (there are, of course, no grade crossings). Railroads require flat grades and wide curves, because of the weight and size of trains. The higher the speed, the more stringent the requirements.

The minimum radius of curvature was fixed at a broad 8,200 feet, except within metropolitan areas where the speed of trains would be reduced. Percent of grade was limited to a low 1.5 (1.5 feet of climb per 100 feet of track). To keep the line, running as it must through hilly, broken country, as straight and flat as these figures demanded, many more tunnels, bridges, and trestles were needed than on the old Tokaido. In fact, of the 320 miles of the whole line, no fewer than 40—more than an eighth of the total—are in tunnels. Another 27 miles run over 281 bridges, in addition to some 60 more miles of trestle. Several of the bridges are major river crossings, the longest, the Fujigawa, nearly 4,000 feet. All are conventional structures of standard design—prestressed and reinforced-concrete girders, plate girders, composite girders, and steel trusses. The Fujigawa is made up of six continuous through trusses and a simple truss. Of a total of sixty-six tunnels, twelve are longer than a mile. The biggest is the New Tanna. Parallel to the Old Tanna and slightly longer, it runs for nearly 5 miles. The old tunnel, begun in 1918, was only finished, after incredible hardships and setbacks, in 1934. The new tunnel also has had a prolonged history, but this is due to a suspension of work rather than to any particular difficulties in the tunneling. Begun during World War II as part of a projected improvement in the existing line, it was abandoned until 1959 when the New Tokaido work commenced. Within three years, it was holed through, and the tunnel was finished in 1963. The second largest tunnel, the Nangoyama, actually gave more trouble, spouting underground water for days in 1960.

The eight long bridges are all built to standardized designs, with considerable use of reinforced and prestressed concrete. The longest, the Fujigawa, rests partly on a pneumatic-caisson foundation and a reinforced-concrete pier, with a superstructure of six through trusses and a simple truss. The caisson was sunk in 1961, the substructure completed in 1962, and the trusses cantilevered into place in the winter and spring of 1962–1963, with completion of roadway in 1963.

The elevated track lies mostly in the metropolitan areas, where embankments would be inconvenient and in many cases prohibitive because of space problems.

Track layouts at the stations are of two types, depending on whether express trains stop. At most of the ten intermediate stops and the Tokyo terminal, the new stations are built adjacent to the old, but at Osaka, a large new station was designed at a distance from the congested terminal of the old line. This station was planned with a further consideration in mind—the possibility that the New Tokaido line may in the future be extended westward.

Roadbed, rails, ties, expansion joints, turnouts (switch points), bridge roadways, and every other detail of railway structure were closely studied and designed for a maximum safe speed. Ties are prestressed concrete; tracks are welded in mile-long sections and laid on a roadbed of crushed stone. Many entirely new design features were introduced. A movable nose rail was added to accommodate switching at points where the maximum speed was to be used. Center-to-center distance between tracks was fixed at 13 feet 9 inches to minimize the air impact of two high-speed trains passing each other, but in station yards, the distance was made larger, because yardmen sometimes are working between the tracks when an express roars by at 125 mph. The distance, determined as that which would keep the wind on the yardman down to 24 mph, worked out to a bit over 15 feet.

The route chosen, the engineering works begun, the roadbed, tracks, and stations laid out, the next problem was the actual operation of the trains. The first question was, how many trains should the line carry? A careful analysis was made of traffic on the old line—number of passengers boarding at each station, their destinations, traveling hours, even why they were traveling. Freight was analyzed as carefully—how it was packaged, how much handling was needed.

Trains were planned to cover the 320 miles from Tokyo to Osaka at three speeds, the programmed speed to be achieved gradually over the first years of operation:

	Time	Average Speed
Superexpresses (16 cars)	3 hours	125 mph
Expresses	4 hours	90 mph
Freight	5½ hours	60 mph

How can numerous trains traveling at such varying speeds as the superexpresses and the freights safely use the same tracks? By a wonderfully simple expedient. The passenger trains run only in the daytime, the freight trains only at night. Ordinary expresses stop at all ten intermediate stations, but the superexpresses, of which twenty run per day, stop only at Nagoya and Kyoto. Facilities to pass are provided at most of the intermediate stations.

Naturally, automation has been applied to every possible aspect of the operation. Nevertheless, the motorman retains a most important role. In starting the train, he operates the handle of a master control. Once the throttle is opened the speeding-up process is carried out automatically until the train reaches its maximum speed, predesignated by an Automatic Train Control device. When a train running at maximum speed nears a station where it is to stop, the Automatic Train Control first slows it down in three stages. At the lowest speed, the motorman takes over, manipulating the pneumatic-brake handle to bring the train to full stop at the designated position. The Automatic Train Control also is used whenever train speed is restricted, though in some cases the motorman's intervention is again necessary.

In general, the Automatic Train Control operates, not to run the train, but to keep its speed within predesignated limits. When a train enters a section where speed must be reduced, the indicator in the cab will signal that a change is to be made, for example, from 200 to 160 kilometers per hour, and if the train's speed at that moment exceeds 160, the Automatic Train Control applies the brakes. As soon as speed is down to the new level, the brake is released, allowing the train to proceed at the new constant speed.

The first test runs were carried out on a short section in June of 1962. The section was typical of the whole line, containing five bridges, eleven tunnels, and about 4 miles of elevated tracks. Preliminary tests were run with two-car trains reaching speeds of about 100 mph. In October, full-scale tests began. Every day, the running speed was increased a little. Finally, on October 31, with engineers and officials crowded into the second car, their eyes glued to the big dial showing train velocity, the motorman was given the green light for maximum speed. The countryside flashed by, the dial needle moved up, to 200, 220, finally to 250 kilometers (160 mph). The speed was held for two minutes, then slackened. Every part of the train and track was then exhaustively examined; each part was found in perfect condition.

The next day tests at maximum speed were resumed. It was found that minor irregularities in the roadbed surface and track level had little noticeable effect on oscillation in the cars, but that imperfect alignment and slight irregularity in gauge did create undesirable motions inside the train. Corrective steps were taken, and the already strict limits established for track irregularities were tightened further. Only one really significant change was made as a result of the test runs. Many of the officials, foreign observers, newsmen, and others complained that their ears hurt when the train entered a tunnel. The solution, simple in conception but rather complicated to carry out, was to airseal every car. Doors were made airtight, and a special signal system was installed, triggering valves to shut airconditioning intakes and exhausts as the train hits the tunnel.

In 1964, regular service was inaugurated in time for the Olympic Games in Tokyo. Most Western passengers were impressed by three things about the ride: first, the speed; second, the picturesque beauty of the countryside (Mount Fujiama is on the route); and third, the comfort of the train's interior.

Though the official name of the express is the Bullet

Train, an apt reference to its snub-nosed shape as well as to its speed, the Tokyo papers call it "The Superexpress of Dreams." Numerous American visitors have reported on its tasteful decor—light-blue glass curtains and darker-blue draperies, both veined with gold, blue carpeting, and gold-upholstered seats—and on its remarkable steadiness at high speeds. A brimful whisky jigger set down on the window sill does not spill one drop. Buffet cars are decorated with a profusion of fresh flowers. Two counters, a standup and a sitdown, serve a variety of Japanese refreshments. In addition, girl attendants trundle wagons of food and cake through the cars. Seats are in conventional pairs in first-class and three-and-two in second-class cars.

The truth is, the comfort and efficiency of the New Tokaido are the significant things about it. The much-trumpeted speed is not quite that amazing. Few of the Americans who have ridden the Superexpress of Dreams and marveled as they translated the 200 kilometers per hour on the big dial in the buffet into 124 mph can be aware of the run made by the first Pennsylvania Special from New York to Chicago June 11–12, 1905. A hotbox having delayed the highly competitive crack train in Ohio, the engineer was given the go-ahead for maximum speed in order to catch up on its schedule. Early on the morning of June 12, the train entered the "Racetrack," a dead-level section of Indiana. In the coaches, Pennsylvania officials checking their stop watches against the 3-mile-apart signal towers broke into exclamations. From AY Tower to Elida had taken just 85 seconds, which was 127 mph.

That speed was attained by a ten-wheel, steam-boiler locomotive hauling a coal tender and four heavy coaches. It was never afterward exceeded by a steam locomotive, or by a Diesel either. Not even an all-electric-power train, such as the Superexpress of Dreams, has improved the mark discernibly in regular operation, though in its test runs it has topped 150 mph. (A French National Railways Mistral did better than 200 mph in a test run, setting a world's record.).

However, in that swaying, plunging, clickety-clacking Pennsylvania Special (which did, by the way, make up the lost time and successfully inaugurate the then astounding 18-hour New York–Chicago schedule) there is no record of anybody setting a brimful jigger of whisky on the window sill. Nor was there then or later, on an American line, a schedule of high-speed trains running half an hour apart over distances of more than 300 miles with split-second exactness. (Ultimately, Tokaido headway will be cut to 15 minutes and timetables discarded.) Continuous fast operation on a crowded schedule, with nonspill comfort and absolute precision—that, rather than rate of speed itself, is the achievement of the New Tokaido.

3
The Biggest Bridge:
The Verrazano-Narrows

OVER THE ENTRANCE to New York Harbor, between Staten Island and Long Island, four fifths of a mile of twelve-lane concrete highway hangs in the air more than 200 feet above the blue water. This feat of levitation demands an explanation. How can you raise 100,000 tons of steel and concrete in the air and make it stay there?

It was not easy. When the late Othmar H. Ammann was born in Switzerland in 1879, the bridge with the longest span in the world was the Honeymoon Bridge, a narrow carriageway 1,269 feet long suspended over the Niagara gorge just below the Falls. It blew down in 1889, when Ammann was ten years old. There was nothing unusual about that. Suspension bridges had always blown down, when they didn't collapse under marching troops, trotting herds of cattle, drifting snow, or their own weight. Some very bright men had fought the problem, because the suspension principle had an irresistible attraction—it was very cheap. Sizable suspension bridges had been built for less than $1,000, but they wouldn't stay up.

The eighty-six years of Othmar Ammann's lifetime saw the development of suspension bridges that stay up. When he first came to the United States in his twenties, fresh out of polytechnic school, Ammann planned on a stay long enough to acquaint himself with American bridge-building methods. Almost immediately he became involved in an investigation of the tragic failure, during construction, of the Quebec cantilever. A cantilever is a balanced form, tapering outward from the bottom like a V and hooked in pairs with a short intermediate span to support a bridge deck. It is troublesome to erect, but once up, it forms a very substantial structure. So does a steel-arch bridge—Ammann built the world's biggest at Bayonne, New Jersey.

A suspension bridge just was not that substantial. It was very easy to put up; back in 1801, Captain Josiah White of Philadelphia hung one over the Schuylkill, which is a good-sized river, on iron-wire cables. Captain White's bridge, 1½ feet wide, anchored to a tree on one side of the river and to a window of Captain White's factory on the other, cost $125. It fell down within a few years. So did any number of others.

Then, a succession of gifted French, British, and American engineers, notably the German-American immigrant John Augustus Roebling, slowly strengthened the wobbly suspension bridge. Their ultimate creation is something you have seen a thousand times, but can you remember how it is built? Try drawing it. You will do well if you remember to put in four elements: towers, cables, anchorages, and a roadway. Most people forget the anchorages, apparently figuring that the cable ends disappear into a hole in the ground. Unless you are an engineer, it is unlikely that you have drawn another element: the foundations. Of course, foundations are more or less implicit in the towers and anchorages—any structure obviously has to

stand on something, but it is very doubtful that if you undertook to draw them you would represent them in anything like accurate proportion. Those foundations go deep
down.

Even supposing you drew towers, anchorages with their
foundations, cables, and a roadway, the odds are about
10,000 to 1 that you missed the sixth major element of a
suspension bridge. This is the truss, the key to the whole
suspension-bridge problem, the indispensable additive that
made this beautiful creation at last stand securely.

What holds a bridge up? You can probably identify the towers,
cables, and anchorages, but can you spot the truss?

The *truss* is a very old piece of engineering geometry,
used by the ancient Greeks. It is based on the fact that a
triangle, unlike a structure of four or more sides, cannot be
distorted. Nail three pieces of wood together, and you can
push and pull till you break something, but you cannot
distort the figure. The truss is used in all kinds of ways in
construction; it can even support a bridge by itself. Most of
the old covered bridges were truss structures, and the forms
developed by the covered-bridge builders of New England
and Pennsylvania survive today as the basic types of most
steel railroad bridges.

For the suspension bridge, the truss does not carry the
main load. It is too shallow for that. Its function is twofold:
first, to prevent the roadway from deflecting downward,
that is, sagging under traffic and its own weight; and sec-

ond, to prevent it from deflecting laterally, that is, distorting sideways under a strong wind. Gradually developed over a period of years by Roebling and others, the truss is the great secret that made the suspension bridge work. Roebling's masterpiece, the Brooklyn Bridge, completed in 1883, was the first of the great modern long-span suspension bridges—strong, beautiful creations that will endure for centuries.

Yet even after the Brooklyn Bridge, there was one last booby trap waiting for suspension-bridge engineers. This was the wind, or more precisely, a certain characteristic of the wind. It is not difficult to make a truss strong enough to withstand a 100 mph gale, or, for that matter, a 150 mph gale. However, the wind has another aspect besides mere force—a peculiarly treacherous one for man-made structures; this is its ability to start a structure swaying. The sway may become complex or take on a twisting motion. Then look out.

At first, as bridges grew longer and carried heavier loads (several turn-of-the-century suspension bridges were built to carry rapid-transit lines), the trusses grew deeper. New York's Williamsburg Bridge set the record with trusses 40 feet deep. Then, Joseph Melan, a brilliant Austrian, developed a new mathematical-engineering theory known as the deflection theory, which permitted much more precise calculation of stress, and the trusses began to grow shallower. This made bridges both cheaper and more beautiful; yet trouble lay ahead. In 1940, the long, slender Tacoma Narrows Bridge over Puget Sound went into a series of wild gyrations in a 42 mph wind and literally tore itself to pieces. By great good fortune, nobody was killed, but many people were considerably embarrassed. The three-

man investigating board, whose chairman was Othmar H.
Ammann, pronounced the bridge guilty of "an extraordinary degree of flexibility" and "a relatively small capacity
to absorb aerodynamic forces."

One serious defect in the Tacoma Narrows Bridge and
many others built at the same time was that the reliable
web truss formerly used had been "improved" by turning it
into a shallow, solid-plate girder. This saved steel; the Tacoma girder was only 8 feet deep. But it created a solid, H-
shaped cross section that trapped wind gusts and reacted to
them like a jump rope.

The failure of the Tacoma Narrows Bridge caused a
good deal of wind to go through wind tunnels in order to
test reactions of trusses and also caused the Bronx-White-
stone and other new bridges to acquire web trusses; the
solid cross section no longer was used. To make it even
easier for wind gusts to blow through a bridge, grid openings were introduced in roadways. As steel and steelmak-
ing improved, truss and roadway sections were fabricated
together in single units, greatly increasing bridge strength.

Another fundamental problem of a more obvious nature
is the excavation and construction of deep foundations. For
decades, the depth of bridge foundations was limited by
man's capacity to survive and work in compressed-air
chambers at the bottom of caissons. These old-fashioned
caissons were simply big iron or steel boxes, open at the
bottom and with a shaft mounted on top, which were
pushed down through the water and then through the mud
by men digging with pick and shovel. However, in the
1930's—notably in San Francisco Bay—a new kind of
caisson was introduced; it was enormous in size and honey-
combed with wells through which digging machinery could

operate. Suddenly, it was possible to build secure bridges in places where foundations had to go to great depths, such as the Narrows of New York Harbor.

New York engineers had been pondering a Narrows crossing for a long time. A glance at the map shows the value of such a crossing:

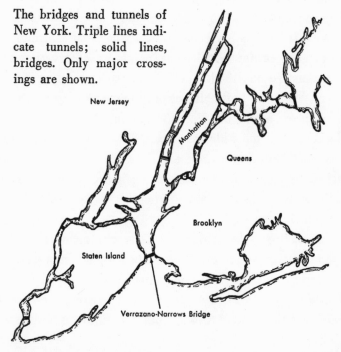

The bridges and tunnels of New York. Triple lines indicate tunnels; solid lines, bridges. Only major crossings are shown.

New Jersey

Manhattan

Queens

Brooklyn

Staten Island

Verrazano-Narrows Bridge

The chain of water crossings around the metropolitan area had one big missing link, for want of which traffic could not flow easily from New Jersey to Long Island and New England without passing through congested Manhattan. At the same time, the last major tract of undeveloped real estate in the area was on Staten Island, and while Staten Islanders liked their rusticity, the inexorable laws of urban growth made it an anachronism.

There were two essential preliminaries. One was to get the permission of the Defense Department, which ruled that the bridge would have to be 216 feet above the channel at mean high water and further that almost the whole channel would have to be kept clear, a consideration that translated into a span length of 4,260 feet, 60 feet more than the Golden Gate. Only a suspension bridge could meet those requirements. The second preliminary was a little matter of money. It has already been said that the great charm of the suspension bridge was its cheapness, an observation that now must be qualified. The Verrazano-Narrows was not a cheap bridge to build. It not only is too long to be cheap, but it is too high (228 feet at midpoint), too deep (double-decked), and too wide (six lanes, 103 feet). Altogether, it cost $325 million, and that is only the price tag, not the actual amount that motorists using it are going to pay in tolls, a sum no man can predict—it might easily be $1 billion.

Financing of the bridge was done with bonds, the bondholders being repaid over a very long period from the tolls. On top of that, the Triborough Bridge and Tunnel Authority, like nearly all United States toll collectors, is markedly reluctant to abandon a toll booth once it has been opened. A Scottish commission once came to New York to study American toll collecting. They expressed great admiration for everything about our procedures except our habit of never quitting. Back home in Scotland, they said, they collected until a bridge was paid for, then stopped.

To take charge of the vast project, one man stood out as the obvious choice—Othmar H. Ammann. Ammann's role in the enterprise may be likened to that of the commanding general of an army in combat. The actual execution of the design was entrusted to Ammann's long-time partner, Milton Brumer. Underneath him were top specialists in the various elements of the work—foundations, towers, overall design—themselves commanding sizable brigades of working engineers, whose mountains of drawings were gradually translated into structural elements at the contractors' plants, shipped to New York, and assembled by the front-line troops at the bridge site.

The work itself began in 1954 in a peculiarly inconspicuous way. Four holes in the ground were bored—or rather, three holes were bored in the ground and one in the water —for the two towers and two anchorages. The holes were to find out how far down solid-enough stuff to plant a foundation on lay. At the Staten Island anchorage site, a sturdy layer was hit 160 feet down. Under the Staten Island tower, 300 feet off shore, it was even farther down, and on the sandy Brooklyn shore under the Brooklyn anchorage, still farther. Deepest of all was under the Brooklyn tower site on Fort Lafayette, a little islet acquired from the Defense Department. Fort Lafayette turned out to be sitting on a pile of sand, clay, and broken rock reaching down 300 feet. The rockbed has never been located in the Narrows Channel.

Twenty-eight more borings carried out in 1956 gave a reliably complete picture of the geology. It was determined that the tower foundations did not have to be sunk to bedrock but could safely be planted in layers of compacted sand and clay above the rock layers. The deepest foundation, that on the Brooklyn shore, had to go down 170 feet. That was enough to demand some fairly extraordinary measures.

Caissons 129 by 229 feet were constructed on small artificial islands built up out of sand in the shallow water to protect the work against the strong Narrows tides. The caisson foundations were divided by bulkheads into nine compartments, with cutting edges on the bottoms of the external and internal walls. On top of this foundation was a superstructure of sixty-six wells, through which clamshell buckets (they look like clamshells) could be operated. The spaces between the wells were filled with concrete to help keep the whole contraption sinking; as the clamshell buckets dug out the mud underneath, the caisson's own weight forced it steadily down.

On top of each tower caisson, when it reached down far enough, were erected the two pedestals for the two legs of the tower. At last, Staten Islanders who had been watching impatiently could see some visible progress. The bridge was "out of the ground."

Thus, although 690 feet high as measured from the water's level, the Brooklyn tower is 860 feet over-all, the equivalent of an eighty-story skyscraper. Its skeleton is made up of some ten thousand steel boxes. These boxes are stacked in a complex pattern, for the cross section is an irregular shape, and the tower shafts taper as they rise. During construction, though all the boxes were lighted, every worker was equipped with a miner's hat and a map so he would not get lost; you could wander for miles on the floors and ladders inside even one shaft of a tower. More than one worker actually did get lost, though most did not like to admit it. Every night the men were counted as they came off the job. Originally, this was applied only to the regular crew, but one night, two outside repair men were temporarily stranded when they could not find their way out, and a complete checkout system was put in.

At the base, each tower leg measures 35 feet 7 inches by 49 feet, and each has an elevator shaft inside it. The completed tower contains just under 27,000 tons of steel held together by more than a million high-strength bolts and triple that number of rivets.

Curiously, though the towers are identical in shape and appearance, they were constructed differently. The Brooklyn tower, fabricated by the Harris Structural Steel Company of New York, used twelve sections to a tier, while Bethlehem Steel made up the tiers of the Staten Island tower in fourteen sections. These sections are of varying numbers of cells (four to six, mostly) and varying weights, depending on just what part of the shaft or strut they occupy. The fabrication jobs were fantastically complex. There is no such thing as a typical section. Every plate, every angle, every hole had to be specified in working drawings. One Bethlehem engineer reported that he knew when the working drawings were finished because the stack of papers was as high as the towers were going to be. To make sure the cells were going to fit together properly, whole major sections of the towers were actually assembled in the shops and then disassembled again for shipping.

The key tool in erecting the thousands of cells into shafts and towers was a rig called a *creeper*, a huge derrick mounted on rails bolted to the tower face. Once a cell was set in place (and imagine the precision needed to make the flanges and holes all meet exactly) there was a return to old-fashioned, individual-craftsman methods. Each cell was bolted from little one-man basket scaffolds, each containing just one man, his tools, and a keg of bolts.

In days gone by, men perished by the score on these bridge superstructures. On the big Firth of Forth cantilever, for instance, more than fifty workmen fell to their deaths or were fatally injured by falling objects. Today, accidents are minimized by better equipment and intensive vigilance. Full-time cleanup crews on the Verrazano-Narrows construction kept all walks, stairs, scaffolds, and open decks free of debris. Even cigarette butts were meticulously swept up. All temporary ladders and walkways were bolted as securely as if they were meant to be part of the permanent structure. The resulting safety record has been remarkable, but not perfect. One man fell to his death from a ladder inside a tower; another, from an approach span; and a third lost his footing on the bridge itself and, before the horrified eyes of his buddies, plunged to death in the water below. Soon after that accident there was a brief strike for safety nets, which the contractors considered less safe than safety belts and rope lines. The men won their point and got their nets, which, during the next year, saved the lives of three.

A word about these men is in order, if for no other reason than to dispel any thought that their demand for safety nets reflects a prudent or apprehensive attitude toward their work. Ironworkers, as they are called though they work exclusively on steel, are among the last of the world's adventurers. Those who worked on the Verrazano-Narrows have been memorialized by Gay Talese in *The Bridge*. They go from job to job, from skyscraper to bridge to tower, making good money, spending it, sometimes going a stretch without a job, sometimes crossing the country or going to Alaska, or South America, or Portugal to find one. Some of them are Mohawk Indians of the Caughnawaga tribe, whose home on the St. Lawrence River became the scene of bridge-building activity at the time of the ill-

starred Quebec-cantilever construction in 1904. The Indians went to work on the bridge, originally as ground-
level unskilled labor, but they soon became ironworkers.
Many of them were among the seventy-five who perished
when the cantilever failed in 1907, but the disaster only
gave them a zest to be daredevils. They worked on bridges
all over Canada, on skyscrapers in New York, on the
George Washington Bridge, the Empire State Building, the
Pulaski Skyway, the Golden Gate Bridge, and hundreds of
other places where pieces of steel had to be steered into
position and riveted together far above city streets or chilly
waters. The skyscraper boom of the 1920's brought a whole
colony to settle in North Gowanus, Brooklyn, but many of
those who worked on the Verrazano-Narrows Bridge, some
of them grandsons of men who died in 1907, drove home
every week end to the old reservation in Quebec Province.
They are remembered still in the Wigwam Bar in Brooklyn.

All ironworkers, of course, are not Indians; Americans
of every extraction and from all over the country worked
on the Narrows. The Irish were well represented, as they
long have been on construction jobs; the most promi-
nent among them on this bridge was John (Hard Nose)
Murphy, the hard-driving, hot-tempered superintendent,
forty years a bridge and skyscraper builder, rising from
ironworker on the George Washington Bridge to top boss
on the Pan American Building and the Verrazano-Narrows
Bridge.

Ground breaking for the tower and anchorage foundations began in August 1959; two years later, in October
1961, tower erection began. Both towers were substantially
completed by the end of 1962, a good thing for the contractors, because these contracts always carry penalty clauses;

each day of tardiness would have cost either Bethlehem or Harris $10,000.

With the towers and anchorages erected, the most picturesque part of suspension-bridge building could begin— the cable spinning. This trick was invented by the French engineer Louis Vicat a century and more ago; Vicat looped a strand of wire around a *traveling wheel* at one anchorage, drew the wheel up a special cable, over the near tower, down and across the stream, up and over the opposite tower, and down to the farther anchorage. There, workmen turned the wheel around, relooped the wire, and sent it back. This is how it is still done today; the hundreds of parallel strands of wire are actually all one long wire. The number of wires naturally depends on the size of the bridge they are expected to sustain. The four Narrows cables, whose erection was carried out by the American Bridge Division of U.S. Steel, have a lot of weight to hold up—100,000 tons. Each cable is made up of 61 strands of 428 wires each—or 26,108 wires, tightly squeezed together.

An indispensable preliminary to cable spinning is the erection of catwalks. They are made up from sections of chain-link fence, folded like accordions. These are hoisted to the tower summit and then given a shove or a kick. The heavy mat slides down the lines, which have been raised to the same sag curve that the cables are to have. As the mat slides, it unrolls, coming to rest at the bottom of the sag. The next mats unroll against it on either side, and so on, till the whole catwalk is in place. It was not exactly like taking a stroll down Park Avenue to walk out on this swaying steel grating, the water 200 feet below, but as bridge catwalks go, this pair was pretty secure.

The Narrows traveling wheels, 48 inches in diameter,

began their 8,000-foot journeys in March 1963. In accord with an old bridge-building tradition, there was fierce competition between the two gangs on the opposing cat-walks. The rivalry began on the morning of March 7, 1963, with the two morning gangs and continued, morning and afternoon gangs, through the months that followed. The wheel made its journey across the water and back in 12 minutes—five times an hour, forty times for an 8-hour shift. That was fast work. But the cheering, shouting, competing gangs on the catwalks soon developed extraordinary speed at grabbing the wheel, pulling it down, grabbing the wire, and clamping it down into its hook and pulley, while the gangs at the anchorages developed similar competitive skills, removing the wire, hooking it, reloading the wheel, and sending it back. One day, one gang moved its wheel back and forth fifty times. At first, nobody could believe this record, but a few weeks later another gang did it fifty-one times. This record was tied, but never beaten. A gang on its way to fifty-three crossings was cruelly disappointed when its engine conked out. Once, a wheel skipped right off the line and came bouncing down the catwalk, almost knocking a man off the bridge.

The four Narrows cables weigh nearly 10,000 tons apiece, or a total of 38,192 tons for 145,000 miles of wire. They are not the thickest of bridge cables, though; the Golden Gate Bridge is held up by just two cables of 27,572 wires apiece. The six-lane Narrows roadway and trusses weigh another 60,000 tons. The total weight of steel in the entire bridge, including approaches, is 210,700 tons. By comparison, the cars, even on a crowded Sunday afternoon, are hardly worth weighing.

The cable-spinning process was completed by the hanging of the cable *suspenders,* the vertical lines that hold up the roadway. Each is gripped to the cable by a *saddle,* a huge steel casting that comes in two halves. One day during erection, one fell into the Narrows, missing a passing hydrofoil boat by an eyelash and the approaching aircraft carrier *Wasp* by barely two minutes. The casting was recovered by divers.

The cables pass over the tower summits on giant saddles of steel and vanish into the anchorages, which like the towers are made up of stacks of steel boxes, but high-strength bolts hold the tower structure together, and 375,000 cubic yards of concrete help hold everything down. The Brooklyn anchorage is sunk 52 feet below the ground, the Staten Island anchorage, 76 feet. When the foundations were dug, the two holes were big enough to accommodate two football fields apiece. The four cables, just under a yard thick, are affixed to steel eye bars in the heel of each anchorage.

With foundations down, towers and anchorages up, and cables spun, the stage was set for the final act. The steel-roadway skeleton and the steel trusses were divided into sixty sections. This design gives exceptional strength against the wind. Each section was a boxlike unit weighing 388 tons. Each had to be barged to the site, hoisted by crane, and hooked up to the suspenders and to the previously erected section. In November of 1963, the first unit was lifted into place at the Brooklyn anchorage. All winter, the work went on—maneuvering the barges into position, hoisting, connecting. A big, barrel-chested supervisor named Red Kelly stood on a barge and ran the operation, using a bull horn to communicate with the men operating the cranes. It took 25 minutes to hoist a unit to where the steel connectors could grab it. The connectors' job was to bang home a few holding bolts till the following crews could do the real connecting.

When they did, the bridge was as good as finished. Approach spans, toll plazas, expressway connections, all were under construction simultaneously with the main project. New York's water-leapfrogging auto-traffic girdle was complete.

And venerable Othmar H. Ammann, together with his Ammann and Whitney associates, the steel company people, Hard-Nose Murphy, Red Kelly, and the Caughnawaga Indians, had set a new world's record. How long will they keep it? Not forever, certainly. The Japanese National Railroads plan a bridge over Tokyo Bay involving a suspended main span just short of 5,000 feet, as well as a bridge over Akashi Strait, opposite Kobe, with a span almost precisely that of the Verrazano-Narrows. The late David Steinman designed a bridge to link Sicily with the mainland across the Straits of Messina that would be more than a mile wide.

A last detail. Some people may ask, who in the world is Verrazano? Bridges, at least in the United States, usually get their names from their location. Often enough, this results in a beauty of a name—Golden Gate, Glen Canyon, Narragansett, Carquinez Strait, Mackinac. The New York Narrows isn't a bad name at all. But somebody suggested honoring the man who in 1524 discovered New York harbor, an adventurous Italian mariner named Giovanni da Verrazano. Verrazano described the harbor as "a very agreeable location" in his report. If he could see it today, with the mighty bridge spanning its broad entrance, he would have no reason to change his sentiments.

A comparison of America's four great suspension bridges, the Verrazano-Narrows, the Golden Gate, the Mackinac, and the George Washington, is interesting. (For more bridge statistics, see the Appendix).

Bridge	Main span	Total suspended structure	Width	Towers	Deepest foundation
Verrazano-Narrows (1964)	4,260 ft.	6,690 ft.	103 ft.	690 ft.	170 ft.
Golden Gate (1937)	4,200	6,450	90	746	115
Mackinac (1958)	3,800	7,400	68	552	210
George Washington (1931)	3,500	4,760	106	595	75

4
The Longest Tunnel:
The Simplon

MOST WONDERS OF CONSTRUCTION ARE recent in date and transitory in character. They simply represent the biggest and newest in a continuing line of creations. Occasionally, though, an enduring exception arises to hold the championship in its class for decades on end.

The Simplon Tunnel, like the Empire State Building, represented the newest in a continuing series. However, its achievement far outran the merely bigger, newer, and more expensive. The Simplon was a daring, even reckless undertaking, a gamble against the odds, and a plunge into the unknown. It was carried to completion by as high a degree of skill and resolution as man can bring to his affairs. Its character as an engineering feat cannot be measured simply by its record length of 12½ miles, the world's longest transportation tunnel. It is the labor itself that makes this piece of work forever memorable. By coincidence, it is also forever lasting, since there will never be a reason for filling in the Simplon Tunnel, as there may eventually be for demolishing the Empire State.

Tunneling, like bridge building, goes far back in history. On the storied Greek island of Samos, archaeologists have recently explored a strange, rocky passage described by Herodotus and built by "Eupalinos, son of Naustro-phos, a Megarian." It was hewn through Mount Castro to supply water for the capital of the tyrant Polycrates in the sixth century B.C. Eupalinos' tunneling crews were two-man teams of slaves, one holding the chisel while the other swung the hammer. Alignment was a problem, as evidenced by the twists and turns and changes in level in the middle, where the headings from either side of the mountain met.

The Romans improved on tunneling with a fire-and-water technique that remained standard practice through the Middle Ages; they built fires against the rock face, then threw water over the hot rock, cracking it. In the seventeenth century, Pierre-Paul Riquet, an imaginative civil servant of Louis XIV, introduced gunpowder to drive a tunnel for a canal. In the eighteenth century, a gifted English mechanic named James Brindley, in the course of building a canal for his employer, the coal-rich Duke of Bridgewater, drove tunnels of up to 1½ miles in length. Brindley ran into some of the problems that anybody tunneling through a sizable elevation in the earth's surface is bound to encounter—water inrushing, ventilation, drilling time.

A mountain is a mass of rock of varying sizes and varying states of decomposition, shot through with springs of water, and given to shifting unpredictably when disturbed. Nearly always its component materials are hard—gneiss, schist, various volcanics. The long two-man iron drills, turning at each stroke of the hammer, made slow progress and needed frequent repairs and replacements. A great number of holes, usually up to seventy or eighty, had to be drilled to a depth of 1 or 2 feet before the gunpowder charges could be planted. Then, after a round was fired, thick, greasy black smoke filled the heading, driving the half-choking men back toward the portal, and every so often a blast would be followed by a sudden inrush of water, often coming in a torrent that drowned the unlucky tunnelers before they could flee.

If a 1½-mile rock tunnel presented difficulties, they disappeared in comparison with those created by a really long tunnel. The long tunnel necessarily passed under a higher peak. The temperature and the pressure from the mass of rock above would be greater. Also, the profile of a long tunnel nearly always eliminates the possibility of intermediate shafts, making it necessary to dig the whole tunnel by means of two tremendously long headings from each end.

When the first visionaries began discussing the digging of tunnels under the Alpine passes early in the nineteenth century, optimistic calculations of forty and fifty years' work were made. With the tools then available, it is difficult to believe that a tunnel such as the 7-mile Mont Cenis (under the Col de Fréjus) could have been completed in less than a hundred years, but improvements were on the way.

First, there was the mechanical drill. A very good one was devised by Thomas Bartlett, an English engineer employed on railroad work in the Apennines. For long-distance tunneling, Bartlett's drill had a serious defect—it was steam powered. Steam cannot be transmitted long distances without a significant loss of power. The solution, to supply the Bartlett drill with compressed air for power, came from a brilliant Swiss professor of physics, Daniel Colladon. A Piedmontese engineer, Germain Sommeiller, successfully worked out the technical details involved in a compressor run by Alpine water power, and mechanized tunneling began. Already (in 1857) work had commenced by hand on either slope of the Col de Fréjus. The first Alpine tunnel was completed in 13 years after surprisingly few difficulties, for by good fortune the *geothermal degree* —measure of the rate at which temperature rises as you go down—in the tunnel's path happened to be favorable, and the heat inside the Mont Cenis Tunnel never was very oppressive. Despite the extreme difficulties of surveying in the Alps, the line laid down by Italian surveyors in 1857 proved remarkably accurate, the error in alignment being less than 1½ feet, and the difference in level between the two headings only a few inches.

Possibly the Mont Cenis was a little too easy, for it encouraged contractors and engineers to tackle the other Alpine passes forthwith, not always with as happy results. On the St. Gothard, more than three hundred workmen died of accident or disease, the latter brought on largely by bad sanitary conditions. On the Lötschberg, a frightful accident killed the entire attack—drilling—crew of twenty-five men when a blast suddenly released the water of the Kander River through a deep sand seam that crossed the tunnel route. Nitroglycerine and dynamite, introduced in the Hoosac Tunnel in Massachusetts in the 1860's, proved valuable in reducing drill time by reducing the number of charges needed but added a fresh hazard. One of the Hoosac superintendents was blown to bits when he took a bath in the dynamite shed inside the central shaft, the rise in the room temperature detonating the explosives.

By the 1890's, rock tunneling was an established if still pioneer science, and the major Alpine passes had been conquered. Simplon remained.

On the border between Italy and Switzerland, the ancient Simplon pass over Monte Leone is the focal point of routes converging from northern and southern Europe. By the 1890's, railroads had long since reached either side of the range, and European commerce stood impatiently poised to complete the vital connection. Nineteenth-century faith in science reinforced nineteenth-century commercial power. The Simplon should and must be tunneled.

The great difficulty lay in the enormous depth at which a Simplon tunnel would have to pass under the crest of the Monte Leone massif—more than a mile. Any lesser depth would mean that the tunnel portals would be above the snow line, and the tunnel would be useless a large part of the year. But at the same time, it becomes hotter the deeper one goes beneath the earth's surface, and the rate at which the temperature rises is not the same in every area. No geologist could forecast the temperature that would have to be faced a mile down inside the Monte Leone, but even the most optimistic estimates exceeded 100 degrees Fahrenheit. Add to this the formidable and totally incalculable rock pressures that could be anticipated, and the Simplon was a job from which modern engineers might shrink. Yet the Simplon Tunnel, driven to completion at the very beginning of this century, remains to this day the longest, deepest transportation tunnel on the earth's rugged face. In any list of modern man's greatest achievements, indeed, in any list of the greatest achievements of man from the beginning, the Simplon Tunnel must be included.

Chosen to command the army that attacked the Simplon was Alfred Brandt, brilliant head of the German engineering firm of Brandt, Brandau, and Company, and inventor of a highly effective new type of drill that produced a bigger, deeper hole in less time. To overcome the severe rock-temperature problem, Brandt developed an entirely new tunneling plan. The standard strategy was to drive a small

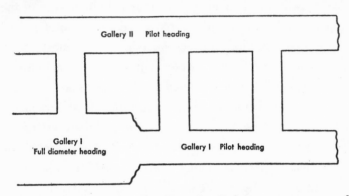

Brandt's plan for the Simplon Tunnel called for two separate galleries, 55 feet apart. Crosshatches between the galleries would provide ventilation.

pilot heading at the top or bottom of the tunnel bore by drilling and blasting, then later to deepen and widen it by hand drilling. Brandt conceived the idea of separating the railroad's two tracks and driving two completely separate *pilot headings*, or galleries, 55 feet apart. One would be left to be finished after the completion and lining of the first. Crosshatches through the intervening rock wall would provide a means for the indispensable ventilation—air could be blown into the portal of Gallery II, through the appropriate crosshatch, and back out through Gallery I. In addition, a nonstop circuit would be provided for the miniature trains bringing drills, explosives, and timbering and lining materials in and carrying rock debris out.

The directors of the Jura-Simplon Railway approved Brandt's plan in 1893, but the complicated political and financial arrangements, which involved the Swiss and Italian governments and the local cantons, were not completed till the summer of 1898.

In the fall of that year, Brandt began assembling his base depots at Iselle on the Italian side and Brig on the Swiss. These resembled the rear area of an army preparing to go into combat. Temporary buildings of all kinds were thrown up—barracks, tool sheds, dynamite sheds, drill-repair shops, locomotive and wagon repair shops, stores, hospitals, kitchens.

While Brandt was assembling his army and its supplies, one of his key aides, Professor Max Rosenmund of the Zurich Polytechnic University, was carrying out reconnaissance on the mountain peak. His first attempt was a failure. So rugged was the ice-encrusted, snow-swept Monte Leone that he was unable to trace the axis of the tunnel on the ground. Triangulation had to be used. A net of eleven points, the highest atop the crest, 11,670 feet above sea level, was laid out. Rosenmund's men built a stone tower at each of the eleven points. Sighting each other from the stone towers, the surveyors laid out the route—and found that their calculations were full of unaccountable errors. Instead of an exact 180 degrees per triangle, their instruments were somehow giving them 180 degrees plus or minus a few seconds. What was wrong? A resurvey produced the same mystifying deviations.

Rosenmund finally figured it out. It was the gravitational field of the mountains themselves, pulling the plumb lines out of their vertical alignments and thus throwing off the angle readings.

This was not the end of the surveying problems. When the surveyors started work inside the tunnel, laying down the line the heading should follow, they ran into an even odder difficulty. A steel frame was erected outside either portal with an adjustable sight set in accordance with the triangulation survey, and a permanent observatory was built behind the backsights. Inside the tunnel, permanent marks were made in the floor every 220 yards.

However, as the heading penetrated the mountain, the curvature of the earth began to produce distortions, and the instruments had to be moved a short distance into the headings. Every 6 months work was halted to let the dust settle so readings could be taken. On one such reading, some 3 miles inside the mountain, a baffling phenomenon took place. The portal opening appeared bent over to one side, as did people entering the portal, and the backsight light appeared double.

The difference in the temperature of the air along the route—it got hotter the farther the heading advanced—produced a difference in density and hence of capacity to refract light. The result was a mirage just like those seen in a desert.

By this time, the tunneling army itself was fully engaged, and the enemy was giving it serious trouble. Alfred Brandt had taken command of the northern task force, that operating from the Swiss heading at Brig. His partner Karl Brandau commanded the Italian heading. But in November 1899, a little over a year after the work began, Brandt died. He had been working almost twenty-four hours a day, and the strain was probably heightened by the fact that although progress was excellent it was slightly behind the rate demanded by his contract. Though a gradual rise in rock temperature was already observed, Brandt could hardly have had any idea of what lay ahead for his successors. Colonel Edward Locher-Freuler, a Swiss engineer, took his place as chief of the northern force.

Each force was driving two headings, one for each of the two pilot tunnels. Three 8-hour shifts worked continuously. Some four hundred men were employed at the start, with the number rising steadily as the mountain was penetrated. In the headings for Gallery II, to be finished later, only an attack crew worked, while in the Gallery I headings a full finishing crew was soon occupied. The attack crew comprised only fifteen men; these operated the Brandt drills, planted the charges, set them off, and cleared out the debris.

A hundred yards or so back, the hand drilling and excavating began, with the crews strung out in a long line. First they dug upward from the pilot heading to the point destined for the crown of the finished tunnel. Then they drove a new short heading in either direction, linking up with each other in this upper gallery. Other crews following behind enlarged these upper galleries to the full width of the upper part of the tunnel.

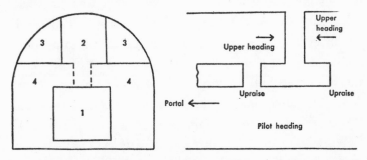

Simplon Tunnel. Diagram on left shows order in which pilot headings were blasted. At right, longitudinal section of heading.

By excavating at the top first, rock could simply be dumped down through the upraises onto the waiting cars, which were hauled out by compressed-air engines. The lower sides, or benches, were then drilled and blasted. During all these operations, timbering supported the roof. Then, the rear guard of the army, the masons, followed, lining the tunnel arch with brick, the sides and bottom with rock or cement.

The first few thousand yards' penetrations by the two converging armies were accomplished with only minor difficulty. Then the temperature began to rise. Thermometer measurements of the rock faces showed 90 degrees Fahrenheit. The rock was warm to the touch. The men, naked to the waist, were sweating profusely in the damp warmth. Water in the springs that were struck from time to time by the attack party began to grow warm, too, and even hot. The water flow was not large, and the drainage canal that Brandt had placed in Gallery II handled it.

Then, on September 1, 1901, the attack crew in the Italian heading suddenly blew the cover off a tremendous spring. A torrent of water gushed out of the cloud of dust. Men dropped tools and ran for their lives. Within minutes the heading was flooded. While Gallery I was still half-filled with water next day, the attack crew in Gallery II hit an even bigger spring, and at almost the same time, a gang digging a cross hatch to release some of the water in Gallery I hit still a third spring. Water was pouring in from three directions at three different temperatures with a flow of 8,000 gallons a minute.

Work was completely disrupted, every man pulled out of the headings. The inrush continued, day after day, rising to 12,000 gallons a minute. Then it slacked off, only to return again in even greater force—13,800 gallons a minute. Week after week the flow continued, months on end; in the spring of 1902, it was still running.

The flood of 1901 gave the southern heading a bad setback, but worse was in store. When the gangs could resume work, they ran into one of the most sinister sections of rock any tunnelers have ever faced—a stretch of micaceous limestone mixed with gypsum and riddled with springs. As the heading penetrated this fragile mass, it turned soft and immediately exerted a pressure that the heaviest timbering could not withstand. Logs 2 feet thick that had just been put in place snapped like matchsticks. The whole heading caved in, and the men once more ran for their lives.

One desperate expedient after another was tried to recover the heading. In the end, the indomitable tunnelers succeeded in bridging the stretch—which was only 137 feet long—by placing a succession of square steel frames, 20 inches thick, one after the other. The frames were screwed together, until seventy-four of them formed a complete tunnel through to the hard rock on the other side of the pressure zone. This inconceivably laborious process took 6 months and set the work hopelessly behind contract schedule. Furthermore, how could they ever break out of this little steel tunnel? That difficult problem was left for the future, and the southern pilot headings were pushed toward the midpoint of the tunnel.

In the meantime, in the northern headings fresh troubles were developing. In the spring of 1902, the rock temperature went over 122 degrees Fahrenheit, and in July it hit 125. The headings were still 2,700 yards from midpoint, but due to the profile of the mountain, these northern headings were to pass under the peak, where maximum heat could be anticipated, before reaching midpoint. The men worked in shortened shifts, pushing through rock whose temperature never dropped below 120 degrees Fahrenheit. The Simplon's geothermal degree, contrary to what geologists had predicted, proved to be very low—40 yards. Rock fragments from the blasting were too hot to pick up. Brandt's two-gallery ventilation system proved invaluable, but working conditions grew more and more unbearable. Through 1902 and 1903, temperatures continued to grow hotter, and frequent water inrushes occurred. In June 1904, water burst in that was so hot it scalded the men before they could jump out of the way.

Because of the heat and the pressure, the rock now began to flake off in bursts, wounding and even killing men in the following crew. The work was suspended, renewed, suspended again. Finally a rock slide wrecked the ventilating system, and the rock walls in the northern headings reached a burning 131 degrees Fahrenheit. At this point, the northern headings had passed the summit. When fresh hot-water inrushes broke in once more, the crews were pulled back, and the last section of the heading sealed up and allowed to fill with water.

Holing through, to join the tunnels, was left to the south crews. They, too, were still struggling. Hot-water inrushes flooded the drainage canal, which had to be enlarged. Cold water was piped from the cold springs farther back to cool the forward part of the heading. In some areas, badly decayed rock required heavy timbering. And all materials, coming in and going out, had to be passed by hand through the narrow steel-framed tunnel in the pressure section.

Even the holing through was a problem because of the waterlogging of the northern heading. When hot springs had first been struck in the northern heading, a special precaution had been taken. The heading, instead of being continued along the bottom of the future tunnel bore, was driven on a slightly rising gradient and then carried along the crown of the tunnel until the water forced a halt. This made it possible for the southern heading to approach from below. When the southern heading of Gallery I was in position directly beneath its northern counterpart, it was evacuated and charges set in the roof. This was in January 1905.

The charges were fired, the rock blew out, and the lake of water that had accumulated in the northern heading came splashing down into the southern one. There was thus no meeting of two crews, shaking hands across the fragmented opening in the middle of the mountain, just water running out of the tunnel—symbolic of the frustrating difficulties that had been conquered.

They were not quite conquered. In the middle of the south heading, that little steel tunnel was still holding back the pressure of the oozy mass of limestone and gypsum. The steel frames had to be removed so that the following crews could finish the tunnel. But how?

There was a good deal of head scratching in Iselle, Brig, and Zurich before a method was figured out. Here is how it was done: A series of small openings was cut in the steel walls. One man entered each such opening and dug downward, till he reached the future *invert* (bottom) of the tunnel. Then the space was filled with blocks of solid cut stone. The difficulty of moving big blocks of stone by hand up through the narrow space of the steel-enclosed pilot heading and maneuvering them to the tunnel floor can hardly be imagined. But once in place they gave the tunnel a strong enough foundation to carry extra-thick walls. Steel "timbering" was then used to break out of the pilot tunnel and complete the excavation. The whole job of finishing this short stretch of tunnel took a year and a half. In January 1906, the inaugural train passed through.

Even then the Simplon's problems were not over. Gallery

II remained to be holed through. A number of difficulties lay in the way—legal problems arising out of the original contract, then World War I, which pre-empted the labor supply (though Switzerland remained neutral, her army was mobilized), and finally, the technical problem of the work itself, which was unique. Never before had such a job—excavating to full diameter a pilot heading 12 miles long—been undertaken. The question, of course, reduced itself to one of efficiency. What was the best way to do it? The engineer in charge, F. Rothpletz of Bern, decided the best approach would be to drill and blast a completely new pilot heading (from upraise shafts all along the line) above the existing pilot tunnel, that is, at the *crown* of the full tunnel. This scheme had a number of advantages, principally, that the excavated material could be dumped quickly into the cars below.

What about the famous pressure zone that had caused such difficulty in Gallery I? Rothpletz decided to attack this zone separately at the very outset, before the approach of the full-diameter excavation could disturb the uncertain rock. Leading a picked crew through Gallery I, he moved into the Gallery II pilot tunnel through a cross hatch. Gallery II had been lined for safety at this point, and it was necessary to remove portions of the top lining to dig out the upper gallery. As the excavation above was being completed, the lower gallery lining was restored, just in case of an accident upstairs. When the upper gallery was completely lined, the lining in between was finally removed for good and the tunnel finished in short order.

Despite such precautions, there were many dangerous rock shiftings before the second tunnel was finished. Sometimes a blast in Gallery II caused a boulder to split, caving in a previously secure section of Gallery I. Sometimes the cave-in was in the other direction. In the southern heading particularly, some 2 miles from the portal a noise like a cannon shot repeatedly preceded a mass of rock ramming into the gallery. In places where the rock was badly decomposed, iron rings similar to those used in underwater tunneling were emplaced in the lining.

Yet another problem arose, a tragic one. While Simplon I had had its share of accidents, the disease rate had been far below that of the St. Gothard Tunnel and some others. However, on Gallery II the new Ingersoll-Rand pneumatic drills had replaced the Brandt water-pressure drills and the result was a great deal of rock dust. In the absence of medical knowledge to prevent it, the deadly lung disease called silicosis struck many workers.

Gallery II was finally completed in 1921. Despite all man's endless digging in the earth's crust in the decades since, the Simplon twins remain his greatest tunneling achievement. If you have never passed through you still can; they are there to stay. However, their status as the world's longest won't last indefinitely. The English Channel Tunnel, which has already captured a record of sorts as the world's most interminably discussed engineering project, will be more than double the Simplon's length. Underwater tunneling is a very different thing from rock tunneling, the problem normally being how to keep the river above safely in its place while performing the rather easy job of digging through the soft ground under it. This can present perils, and subaqueous tunneling has as tragedy-ridden a history as rock tunneling. But in the case of the English Channel, no compressed air is needed to balance the hydrostatic head above; the Channel bed is chalk—easy to bore through but impervious to water. The job would have been carried through long ago, save for the British War Office's apprehensions.

As far as engineering goes, from the Simplon to the Channel Tunnel is from the heroic to the merely interesting.

5
The Tallest Building:
The Empire State

FEW AMERICANS are unable to name the world's tallest building. Yet in 1930, almost no one thought that the Empire State Building's soaring title was more than a momentary thing. The skyscraper race had lent an invigorating note to the booster spirit. The Woolworth Building, Farmer's Trust, Bank of Manhattan, Chrysler, Empire State—what would be next? The record had risen from sixty floors to seventy to eighty to a hundred-plus. As late as October of 1930, Al Smith was still keeping the ultimate height of the Empire State Building a secret, though the basic eighty-six floors were almost completed. The sixteen-story capping tower was in fact an alteration made at the last minute by John J. Raskob, a du Pont partner and Al Smith's backer in this enterprise as in the 1928 presidential election. "It needs a hat," was Raskob's comment when shown the scale model of the original eighty-six-floor structure. The hat would lift it decisively above the new, not quite completed Chrysler Building. So numerous were the dizzy towers of the new age that many New Yorkers expressed concern lest their island sink under the weight of steel and concrete, an apprehension engineers relieved by pointing out that the material excavated for a skyscraper's foundation weighed more than the structure itself.

How tall could a building be built? The newspapers of 1930 printed widely varying calculations, but the American Institute of Steel Construction gave an authoritative-sounding 2,000 feet, nearly two hundred stories.

No one doubted that such heights would soon be achieved. The next step was already publicized—an anonymous cigar magnate was planning a 1,600-foot-tall building, over one hundred and fifty floors, and there were plenty of projects on slightly less grandiose scales.

That was in 1930. Then came 1931; the tower was topped out far above Fifth Avenue and Thirty-Fourth Street, and the opening ceremonies held, with Al Smith, Raskob, Mayor Walker, and many top hats. Tenants began moving in. Then they stopped moving in. Vast office spaces looking down majestically on midtown Manhattan lay empty and silent. Nobody needed them. The Empire State Building was a bust. No more plans for bigger, taller buildings were published. The anonymous cigar magnate was not heard from. The skyscraper race had suddenly ended before the finish lines. It was thirty years and one world war later before anybody started talking again about a building higher than the Empire State.

The skyscraper rush started with steel, for a skyscraper is a steel skeleton curtained by brick and glass. The curtain is of no structural significance. It can be anything—stone, wood, aluminum, or cardboard. The moment steel became available, skyscrapers were possible, and as soon as tall buildings could be built, they went up—and up and up.

Originally buildings had been held to heights of three,

four, or five stories by the limited endurance of their stair-climbing tenants. Then the elevator, first run by steam on a screw shaft and later greatly improved by the development of the electric motor and a suspension design, pushed building heights to nine, ten, even twelve stories. But as their solid-masonry walls rose, they grew thicker at the base, until the first-floor walls were taking up an appreciable amount of the available space and costing a small fortune.

A remarkable signpost of the future had been built as early as 1851 in London, where Joseph Paxton is supposed to have gotten the idea for a *cage* construction from seeing his young daughter stand on a lily pad. Utilizing the umbrellalike rib design of the lily pad, Paxton gave the London Exposition its distinguishing feature, the celebrated Crystal Palace. It was thirty years before the Crystal Palace principle was adapted to commercial buildings, but in 1883–1885, a structure on the northeast corner of La-Salle and Adams Streets in Chicago, the present site of the Field Building, introduced a revolution. This was the Home Insurance Building, and its ten stories, carried by a metal skeleton partly imbedded in its exterior walls, were the creation of William Le Baron Jenney, a California Forty-Niner who had helped build the railroad across Panama and had risen to the rank of major on Sherman's staff during the Civil War. Coming home early one night from his downtown-Chicago office, legend has it that Jenney startled his wife, who jumped to her feet, dropping the book she was reading on a bird cage. What the cage was doing on the floor is not clear, but Jenney, it is said, observed the success with which it withstood the shock of the book and decided then and there that a cage construction would support the floor loadings of a building. Though the story may be apocryphal, Jenney's conception was a bold one, and the Home Insurance Building is generally considered the original skyscraper, although it was never, even after the addition of an eleventh and twelfth floor, the tallest building in the world. By the time its extra floors were put on, the Tacoma Building, also in Chicago, had outstripped Jenney's creation in height and design. In the Home Insurance Building, the outside walls, 4 feet thick on the ground floor, had supported themselves, with the metal columns and girders carrying only the floor loads. In the Tacoma, on the northeast corner of LaSalle and Madison, built by Holabird and Roche in 1887–1888, the skeleton carried nearly all the loads, including those of the brick walls fronting the street. Back and court walls were still self-supporting.

The skeletons of these two Chicago trail blazers were composed of both iron and steel. Jenney used wrought iron for the beams of the lower floors and steel on the upper, possibly because steel first became available during the building's very construction. The columns were of cast iron. This was the first use of steel in a building, though not the first in a structure, James Eads' St. Louis Bridge having been completed a decade earlier.

The French architect-engineer Eugène Emanuel Viollet-le-Duc was the first to perceive the almost limitless possibilities of skeleton-frame construction in metal. Leroy S. Buffington, a Minneapolis architect, after reading Viollet-le-Duc's exposition, designed a twenty-eight story building in 1888, which he nicknamed a "cloudscraper." Buffington's cloudscraper was never built, but the next year another engineer familiar with Viollet-le-Duc's theories built a skeleton of iron that astounded the whole world. This was

Alexandre Gustave Eiffel, one of Europe's leading bridge engineers, who was invited by the French government to create a symbol for the Paris Exposition of 1889, the centenary of the French Revolution.

The conception of the Eiffel Tower was breathtaking; it was an even 300 meters high, 984 feet. Nothing remotely like it had ever been made by man. The Great Pyramid rose only 481 feet. The spire of the Rouen Cathedral, for six centuries the highest thing in France, measured only 495 feet. The dome of St. Peter's in Rome was only 457 feet. All these soaring wonders had taken decades, even centuries to build, had employed thousands of laborers, squandered treasure houses of money, and used up mountains of building materials. Eiffel threw up his airy creation in a few months, with a small crew of a new kind of laborer, and for a trifling cost—$1,200,000. Most remarkable of all, its 984-foot height took a total of less than 7,000 tons of material. Here indeed was a building revolution.

The Eiffel Tower was strictly a demonstration. Now the question arose, how tall could actual buildings framed by metal cages go? The next year, 1890, saw the twenty-one-story Masonic Temple in Chicago capture the title of "tallest building in the world." The Masonic's skeleton was entirely steel, both beams and columns. New York hastened to get into the skyscraper business (exactly when this word came into use is not known) with several interesting buildings. Two of the most famous, long landmarks of Manhattan, are the Flatiron Building, erected in 1902, and the Times Building (recently remodeled as the Allied Chemical Building), in 1904. Both have odd, trapezoidal floor plans, dictated by the pie-shaped real-estate slices Broadway strews along its diagonal path as it crosses Manhattan avenues, Fifth at Twenty-Third, site of the Flatiron, and Seventh at Forty-Second, site of the Times. The resulting slenderness of the two buildings, plus the absence of scientific data on wind stresses, caused the New York engineers to take special precautions. Triangular "gusset plates" were inserted as braces, four to each joint of horizontal beam and vertical column.

The twenty-story, 286-foot-high Flatiron (whose nickname may be a puzzle to modern housewives who have never seen an old-fashioned flatiron) and the twenty-two-story, 375-foot-high Times Building were soon surpassed, first by the thirty-two-story, 468-foot-high City Investing Company Building in Wall Street, then the forty-seven-story, 612-foot-high Singer Building, and climactically, in 1913, by the memorable Woolworth Building. There was something peculiarly appropriate about the Woolworth Building as a symbol of America. American business, mass-production minded and consumer oriented, cornucopia of inexpensive merchandise for every man, woman, child, and dog, was especially well represented, in the eyes of European intellectuals of that day, by the ten-cent store. And in 1913, a year that might be taken as the end of the nineteenth century, the headquarters of the ten-cent chain rose above the hubbub of lower Manhattan Island, sixty stories high, 746 feet up from the ground. This was just 28 years after Jenney's Chicago Home Insurance Building and 24 years after Gustave Eiffel's Paris tower had lighted the way. The skyscraper was here for sure, not an idea or a skeleton, but a building full of people working at desks and typewriters, stacked up in offices, floor by floor, layered one above the other so high that people, horses, wagons, and automobiles below, everyone said, looked like ants.

Many problems had to be solved before the Woolworth Building could be built: plumbing, electricity, heating, ventilation, fireproofing, building maintenance, window washing, mail delivery, long-distance elevators, and many more. The facility with which steel girders could be riveted together into a building skeleton, and the amazing capacity of the structure to withstand stresses, put considerable pressure on all kinds of fabricators, engineers, designers, and production superintendents. There was one problem that nobody could immediately solve. If you filled a square mile of New York with sixty- and seventy-story buildings, where would all the people fit when they went down into the street during their lunch hours? Or at nine o'clock in the morning coming in, or six o'clock going home? New York streets were already crowded in 1913, especially in the downtown areas where the skyscraper boom was on. Since that time, they have become steadily more crowded and no real solution is yet in sight. A negative, but effective, palliative was a 1916 zoning ordinance specifying setback design for high-rise buildings. At the same time, the elevator core was becoming an inhibiting factor. For a thirty-story building, at least two banks of elevators are needed, one to service the lower floors and one the upper, and two banks of, say, six elevators each take up much valuable space. The express elevators in a real skyscraper steal space from all the floors they pass by, and the higher the building the more space they steal. Worst of all, the space loss is largest on the ground floors, which command the best rents.

The problems involved in high-rise buildings are such

that one is prompted to ask, why build skyscrapers in the first place? The obvious answer—to economize on ground space in a crowded metropolis—is too simple. There was plenty of room in lower Manhattan at the time the Woolworth Building was built, and throughout the skyscraper boom of the 1920's there was still room in lower and midtown Manhattan. Even today, if all buildings on the island were of uniform height, they would only have to be about eight stories high to accommodate all the office and residential space presently used. The real reasons behind what might be called the First Skyscraper Boom were apparently three.

First, despite the telephone and such later innovations as teletypewriters and closed-circuit television, a good deal of business must be transacted face to face. For this reason, businesses tend to congregate by industry, the financial industry in Wall Street, the communications industry in midtown Manhattan, and so on. This effect of convenient concentration can best be achieved by very large buildings.

Secondly, the shape of most city blocks, notably in New York, does not lend itself to large-based buildings. A large building fronting on Fifth Avenue must necessarily be tall. The obviousness of this is a little deceptive. The biggest commercial building in the world is still the Merchandise Mart in Chicago, with 4 million feet of floor space. The Merchandise Mart is only eighteen floors high, plus a tower, but it has an enormous frontage of 724 feet along Kinzie Street and 577 feet along the Chicago River. The only larger office building is the Pentagon, built on open land in Arlington County, Virginia, whose five-floor pentagons, nested one inside the other, contain 6½ million square feet. All these human-inhabited structures are dwarfed by one at Cape Kennedy designed for habitation by the Saturn V rocket and enclosing 125 million cubic feet in its four assembly bays. It is beyond all comparison the world's biggest building, but by no means the world's tallest; it is only 526 feet high.

Finally, transportation terminals promote concentration. Grand Central Station is hemmed in by a circle of giants —Chanin, Lincoln, Chrysler, Graybar, Pan Am—somewhat to its aesthetic disadvantage, but from the point of view of New York Central and New Haven railroad commuters, natural enough.

Yet when all is said and done, there is something rather mystifying about the skyscraper. If New York were to be rebuilt from scratch on a rationally planned basis, there might be none. The skyscraper has been called a product of a competitive and anarchic economic society, and it is interesting to note that the boom of the 1920's had strong overtones of status rivalry. The Bank of Manhattan Building, under construction in 1929, kept a very jealous eye on its Lexington Avenue rival, known, before purchase of plans and site by Walter P. Chrysler, as the "Reynolds Building." Originally designed to rise only forty-seven floors, the Bank of Manhattan Building was gradually revised upward to sixty-three, and ultimately to seventy-one, with several modifications coming after construction had actually begun. The giant at 40 Wall Street was topped out with a 50-foot flagpole to carry it to 925 feet, which still left it short of the Eiffel Tower. Chrysler had his architects design a distinctive, if slightly bizarre, lid for his champion, a "finial tower" of spiraling steel plates, which added another 185 feet to the building's basic 845 feet and enabled it to surpass the Eiffel. The plate sections of the tower were lifted one by one up along the outside of the building, over the top of the sixty-sixth floor, and set down inside, in the middle of the sixty-fifth floor. There they were put together and the whole assembly hoisted in one 27-ton piece and its supports placed under it. With its sixty-six true floors and six "penthouse" floors, the Chrysler Building is seventy-two stories high.

Al Smith's original announcement had described the Empire State Building as "close to 1,000 feet high," and though there was some talk of making the Chrysler Building taller, it was soon conceded that the Empire State's basic eighty-six floors would put its summit out of reach. *Engineering News-Record* greeted the new building with the somewhat restrained comment that greater convenience for tenants and more floor space could be achieved by other designs but that the new building would at least test the utility of such slender-tower types. Less technical circles were far more enthusiastic. Despite the market crash and the "slump" as it was optimistically labeled, "Al Smith's new building" was the talk of New York in the winter of 1929.

The first step was one that had already become a commonplace of American urban life, though it still awed Europeans—the demolition of a perfectly good old building to make room for the new one. In this case, the old building was not only sound but distinguished; it was the Waldorf-Astoria, America's most famous hotel. Five months—from October 1929 to the end of February 1930—were required to take its 15,000 tons of iron and steel apart, reduce the masonry to rubble, and haul it all away in sixteen thousand truckloads. Well before the last truck had rolled away, the second step was under way. This was excavation. Contrary to what many New Yorkers think, Manhattan is by no means a solid piece of bedrock. Foundation problems on New York buildings have been numerous. Very often engineers have had to resort to the bridge-builders' tool, the pneumatic caisson, to get through soft ground. To make it a little harder, the soft ground is frequently water bearing. The Empire State site proved very good. On the other hand, the hole in the ground had to be large. Excavation of 9,000 cubic yards of earth and 17,398 cubic yards of rock, carried out by power shovel and hand labor between January 22 and March 17, created a space 55 feet deep, enough for a basement and subbasement. On April 7, with a goodly turnout of sidewalk superintendents on hand, the first steel columns were erected.

By this time, steel erection had been thoroughly mastered. Yet every building presented the same problems in slightly varying form, and the bigger the building the bigger the problems. They may be summarized under four headings: 1. Steel supply (fabrication and delivery of structural members); 2. Plant layout (number and position of derricks and hoisting engines); 3. Steel-handling methods; 4. Erection procedure (setting, fitting up, riveting).

As is commonly done on supersized jobs, two contractors were brought in for the steel erection, McClintic-Marshall and American Bridge Company, subsidiary of United States Steel. The construction was divided between them in a rather unusual way—in alternate layers, each consisting of from one to four "lifts," each lift being the steel members of two floors. On the first ten floors, where the building ran its full width from Thirty-Third to Thirty-Fourth Streets, the contractors' layers were single lifts of two floors each. As the building rose through successive setbacks, the layers were increased.

McClintic-Marshall and American Bridge set up a huge joint supply depot at Bayonne, New Jersey, across the bay. By April 7, the big column sections—H beams and I beams —were stacked in great tidy piles. Movement to the site was carried out with military precision, for there was no room at the busy Fifth Avenue intersection for any overflow of materials and no patience with delays either. Lighters picked up the steel at Bayonne just two days ahead of erection and lugged it across the bay and around the corner of the island into the East River, where it was unloaded at piers at Twenty-Third Street and at Nineteenth Street. The heaviest members were unloaded at the former, the lighter ones at the latter. Trucks ferried the beams uptown to Thirty-Third Street, then west to the Fifth Avenue site. Thirty-Third Street rather than Thirty-Fourth was used primarily because the sidewalk of the latter is exceptionally broad, and in the early stages of construction, when the derricks were down in the bottom of the excavation hole, they could not reach a truck on Thirty-Fourth Street. Other materials were unloaded inside the building itself to keep the dust out of the street. Rubbish was dumped down a steel-plate chute reaching every floor, a truck standing always at the bottom of the chute.

A continuous, almost split-second delivery schedule having been achieved, the next step was plant layout. There were nine derricks in the basement, four at the corners and five in the middle. The four corner derricks were of lighter capacity—rated at 20 tons, though capable of lifting a good bit more. The five middle derricks, rated at 30 tons, could actually lift 50. The biggest loads that had to be moved actually weighed 44 tons, but these, the half-sections of the bottom columns in the core of the building, did not have to be lifted very high. Sidewalk superintendents might take note of the fact that derricks and hoists sometimes do have accidents. Just a few months before work began on the Empire State Building a hoist operator on the Chrysler Building was knocked out by a falling brick and dropped a load of steel.

The Empire State derricks were powered by electric hoists initially positioned in the basement. As work progressed, their hoist lines had to reach higher and higher to the floors being constructed above them. For this purpose, holes were left in the concrete floor slabs, which were being placed as soon as steel erection had gone up to the next floor. This was done not only in the interests of speedy concrete erection, but to facilitate the steelwork. Even the unfinished top floors were given temporary planking to provide firm footing for the riveting and erection crews.

Within the building, an industrial-railway setup was used, with 4,000 feet of straight portable track, 360 of curved, thirty-one turntables and six portable switches. Twenty-four dump cars and twenty-four platform cars ran on the constantly shifted tracks. Material, brick or stone, for example, was dumped from truck to hopper, fed from hopper to dump car, hauled to a material hoist in the center of the building, lifted to the right floor, pushed off on the track, and hauled to the spot where it was needed. This automation represented an enormous speed advantage over the old-fashioned wheelbarrow of earlier skyscrapers.

When steel reached the sixth floor, where the first, and major, setback was designed, the hoist engines were lifted to the second floor. There they remained until the derricks were on the twenty-fifth floor, when they were trussed up and lifted on the outside of the building to that floor. When the steel reached the fifty-second floor, the three smaller, 80-horsepower hoists were moved up again to the fifty-second. But the two biggest, 100-horsepower hoists stayed down on the twenty-fifth because the setback at the fifty-second floor put the derricks out of reach of the unloading trucks on Thirty-Third Street. Consequently, a relay station had to be set up on the twenty-fifth floor and the steel sent up in two moves.

In putting the steel pieces together, three steps were involved. First, the columns and beams were maneuvered into proper position by the steel connectors, the topmost workers in a high-iron gang. Then they were "fitted up" by bolting, and finally, they were riveted solidly together by the riveting gangs. To minimize the number of bolts needed, and consequently the time taken, the riveting gangs were organized to follow closely on the erection crews, working just one floor below them. In the first weeks of construction, an average of two lifts—four floors—a week was maintained. At the end of each lift, the five derricks had to be hoisted to the next platform, two stories higher. This was a 3-hour job.

Until the twenty-sixth floor, three hundred ironworkers were kept busy. After the twenty-fifth-floor setback, the smaller working area could only accommodate two hundred and fifty. Each riveting gang consisted then as today of a riveter, a heater, a bucker-up, a catcher, and a helper, or "punk." The heater, bucker-up, catcher, and riveter passed red-hot rivets, in a popular metaphor, like a baseball infield. The heater toasts the rivet glowing red on his little stove, then tongs it 20, 30 feet or farther to the catcher, who fields it neatly with his bucket (nowadays a metal mitt) and extends it to the bucker-up, who "bucks" it into the hole while the riveter, from the other side, flattens its nose with a rattling volley from his gun.

While the ironworkers lifted the big pieces from the street and riveted them together into a cage, the concrete, stone-facing, and metal-trim crews went to work a few floors below. These specialized crews laid what ultimately came to over 62,000 cubic yards of concrete reinforced by 3 million square feet of steel-wire mesh. They affixed 300 tons of stainless-steel window trim and 450 tons of aluminum *spandrels,* the facing between the top of one window and the sill of the one above. The rest of the curtain, covering most of the vast steel skeleton, was blocked in with 200,000 cubic feet of Indiana limestone. Finally, 10 million bricks were laid, mostly in places where they don't show.

In applying the limestone curtain, the builders made use of experience on previous skyscrapers where breaking, or *spalling,* of stone had occurred. Sometimes temperature drops caused steel members to contract enough to put additional pressure on the stone, or steel members were compressed by unexpectedly heavy floor loadings, or temperature changes affected the facing but not the interior structural members. Occasionally, wind stresses produced cracking. Settling and even vibrations from trains and subways occasionally led to damage.

For the Empire State Building, a specially designed "cowing pressure-relieving joint" was used on each floor. A corrugated sheet-lead filler enclosed in a sheet-lead envelope, the joint is placed at corners where vertical piers and horizontal girders meet and acts like a spring, flexing with whatever overpressure or underpressure may be given by changes in loading, temperature expansion and contraction, and wind force. All the Empire State's relieving joints together can absorb a vertical compression of 6 inches.

The ironworkers formed the vanguard, working always on the open top floor in sun, rain, and wind. Closely behind came the battalions of stonemasons, bricklayers, concrete layers, and trim crews. Still farther down worked the rear echelon of this vertically advancing army, a vast number of specialists. The ten service elevators, two of which were salvaged from the Waldorf, were replaced by the seventy-four permanent elevators, whose 1,200 feet-per-minute speed in their 7 miles of shafts prompted newspaper columnist Bugs Baer to comment that riding them would make one realize how a post card felt in a mail chute. Heating crews installed sixty-seven hundred radiators. Telephone men put in 17 million feet of wire. Plumbers installed 51 miles of pipes. Ventilation crews put in blowers and ducts capable of pulling over 1 million cubic feet of fresh air per minute into the building. (Air-conditioning installations came later.) Every one of these installations established size records, most of which remain unbroken.

At one point, thirty-five hundred men were employed. The peak payroll was $250,000, which works out to an average of about $70 a week, not a figure to make present-day New York construction workers long for the good old days. But by the standards of 1930, the pay was good and considerable pains were taken with the men's well-being. Water-supply and sanitary equipment were of course installed on a temporary basis, and cafeterias were set up as needed. This was relatively easy since each floor was completed as rapidly as possible after the steelwork. The first cafeteria was on the third floor; the next on the ninth, then on the twenty-fourth, then the forty-seventh, and finally the ironworkers were munching sandwiches and drinking hot coffee on the sixty-fourth floor, setting a record for the world's highest restaurant. Elevators also increased in number and height as the job progressed. (The seventy-four elevators are capable of handling fifteen thousand passengers per hour, despite which a team of Polish mountain climbers preferred to use the stairs, climbing the 1,860 steps in 21 minutes.)

The command post for the army of workers was in a long wooden shed built out over the Fifth Avenue sidewalk. There, John W. Bowser, veteran superintendent for Starret Brothers and Eken, the main contractors, directed four divisions: construction, accounting, administration, and project management. This last was the general staff of the task force, receiving the plans from the engineers and architects, and translating them into action in steel and concrete.

Bowser and his assistants, while proud to be building a building taller than anyone else's, were prouder still to be building faster than anyone else ever had. They were right. Although the Empire's height record is due at long last to be broken, its speed record remains untouchable. The last rivet was heated, tossed, caught, and rattled home just twenty-three weeks after the first truckload of steel was delivered at Thirty-Third Street. The masonry job was complete in 8 months. In one 10-day period in the fall, the building jumped fourteen floors—steel, stone, concrete, and everything else. The architects actually had trouble providing detailed designs to keep up with the men; steel was up thirty stories before final plans were ready for some of the lower floors. Some of the steel was rolled into beams, shipped to the Bayonne depot, barged to the East River, trucked to Thirty-Third Street, and hoisted in the miniature railroad cars to the working floor in a total of 18 hours, incredible though that may sound.

The steel was topped out 12 days ahead of a closely figured schedule. The exterior limestone was completely set 13 days ahead of schedule. Yet no overtime was necessary, and the men worked only a regular 5-day week. They put in a total of 7 million man-hours over a period of 1 year and 45 days. It was a fantastic accomplishment, though still another record held by the job is even more fantastic. This is the cost. Since costs normally are always on the rise, the common story of engineering achievements is that they cost from a little to a lot more than their original estimates. This situation can be taken for granted, but the Empire State, launched on the very morrow of the market crash and driven to its breakneck completion while the country sank into the depression, showed an astonishing reversal of form. Figured to cost a round $50,000,000, it ended up at just $40,948,900, of which $24,718,900 was for the building work, the rest for acquisition, demolition, and so on.

New York was proud of the shining new queen of sky-scrapers, though her reputation was tarnished for some time through no fault of her builders. The depression left her half-empty for several years, and the words "white elephant" were murmured, outside of Al Smith's hearing. However, with the arrival of the affluent society, the Empire State Building more than vindicated Al Smith. Today, she has fifteen thousand tenants, many of whom can see the world's most magnificent view on sunny days, and an impenetrable gray wall on foggy ones.

The observation tower, it will be recalled, was an

eleventh-hour decision of John J. Raskob. Without it, the building would have topped the Chrysler by only a few feet. Nobody in 1930 could think of a good reason for adding 200 feet to the building's height, but Raskob insisted, and the tower was added, theoretically as a mooring mast for dirigibles. These sausage-shaped monsters are so forgotten today that it comes as a bit of a shock to recall that they were perfectly serious competitors of the airplane in 1930. During this era, the *Graf Zeppelin* made several trips across the Atlantic as a regular commercial service. However, even if the lighter-than-air ship had proved to be the transportation of the future, it is extremely doubtful that the Empire State Building could have contributed to its success. The whipping winds 1,250 feet above Manhattan made delicate maneuvering of a dirigible impossible, but Raskob's "hat" was added—600 tons of steel erected and riveted into sixteen stories in 17 days of January 1931, in the teeth of treacherous north winds accompanied by freezing rain and fog. A four-story 47-foot-high base was capped by a 105-foot shaft and a circular top piece 53 feet high and 32 feet in diameter. The top two stories were given additionally heavy bracing because to the end the fiction was maintained that Count Zeppelin's giant namesake would tie up there.

An attempt was even made—once—to use the tower for its stated purpose. Not a dirigible, but a blimp—a smaller, balloonlike lighter-than-air craft—was flown up to the mooring mast, but a gust of wind put an end to the experiment and very nearly to the experimenters, who included the usual quota of celebrities. Valiantly striving to execute its balancing act, the blimp released water ballast, which did not enable it to achieve the desired stability, but which

bewildered shoppers on Fifth Avenue, who were drenched
by rain from a cloudless sky. That was the end of the attempt to make the observation tower a hitching post.

The beacon atop the Empire State's tower has served as
a valuable guidepost for aircraft—though fears that a
plane might crash into the building were justified one
foggy day in 1945, when an Air Force B-25 bomber struck
the seventy-eighth and seventy-ninth floors. Eleven persons
in the building were killed, twenty-seven injured. Structural damage was slight.

A lucrative and important, though quite unforeseen, use
for the tower was found, and surprisingly early. In 1931,
only 6 months after the building's inauguration, an experimental station was opened on its top for a new electronic
toy known as television. Owned by NBC, the station presented its first commercial show 10 years later, in 1941.
When commerical television really became a fact after
World War II, NBC agreed to share the Empire State tower
with other broadcasters, and in 1949 the interested parties
agreed to build a tower on top of the tower, a 222-foot-high
needle that would accommodate five TV stations (since
grown to eight) and six FM radio channels. A lightning rod
was thoughtfully added—it's been struck thousands of
times—as well as red aircraft-warning lights. Work on the
antenna was begun on July 27, 1950, and completed on
May 1, 1951, not a particularly gaudy record in comparison with those of the original builders. The cost was $3
million, or nearly an eighth the expense of the original 102
stories.

The tower has another function, and a very valuable
one. It is close to being New York's premier tourist attraction. Visitors can get a magnificent view of city and harbor

from the lower, eighty-sixth-floor Observatory (visibility
40 miles), and a positively awe-inspiring one from the circular, glass-enclosed summit Observatory on the top floor
(visibility 80 miles). Celebrities have their pictures taken
by news photographers; ordinary tourists, by each other.
Many find it a thrill to record their voices this high up, and
others consider it a particularly romantic place to kiss a
girl. Many a motion picure has included a scene filmed in
one of the two observatories.

Among the questions most frequently asked of the guides
by visitors is one that is peculiarly difficult to answer: Does
the Empire State Building sway in the wind? Engineering
Professor J. Charles Rathbun of the City College of New
York made a study in the 1930's and reported in the 1940
Transactions of the American Society of Civil Engineers
that the building has two separate motions in the wind—it
"deflects" and it "vibrates." The deflection of the top of the
building amounts to as much as 10 inches in a strong wind
of 55 to 90 mph. At the same time, it is also vibrating, that
is, moving back and forth at a rate of six to eight times per
minute, by up to 2 inches per vibration.

The antenna brought the total height of the building up
to 1,472 feet, emphatically reaffirming the world's record,
440 feet beyond the reach of the Chrysler Building, and
almost equally beyond the tip of the Eiffel Tower, which
itself has acquired a TV antenna. However, the Empire
State Building is officially listed at merely the basic 1,250
feet. Why this modesty? Because if TV antennas are to be
considered parts of structures, then why should they not be
considered as structures by themselves? In Columbus,
Georgia, there is a TV mast 1,749 feet tall, and in Fargo,
North Dakota, a brand-new one breaks 2,000 feet. Even the

Russians are reported to be building one in Moscow far overtopping the pinnacle of Fifth Avenue.

The Queen of Skyscrapers is in imminent danger of losing her true title, that of being the tallest inhabited building in the world. The wonder is that she has managed to keep it so long. Initially, she ruled through absence of competition as the depression drove real-estate promoters to cover. Postwar affluence brought a construction boom in New York that put the original skyscraper boom in the shade. Few of the new breed of skyscrapers were really tall, most of them stopping at a mere thirty or forty stories. One of them was monstrous (aesthetically as well as otherwise, according to some critics)—the Pan Am Building, which captured the title of "world's largest commercial office building," with its 2,700,000 square feet ranking only behind the Pentagon and the Merchandise Mart. But its squat fifty-nine stories rise only 830 feet above Park Avenue.

The interesting challenger for the title of world's tallest building is the Port of New York Authority's World Trade Center near the lower tip of Manhattan. A magnificent civil-engineering and structural conception, it will consist of immense twin towers one hundred and ten stories high, rising 1,350 feet and topping the Empire State at last.

Designed by the distinguished architect Minoru Yamasaki of Detroit, the towers will have many unusual features, including an elevator transfer system via "sky lobbies" at the forty-first and seventy-fourth floors, where passengers will switch from expresses to locals as in the subway. However, the most remarkable feature by far lies in the basic structural design. It is the work of the Seattle firm of Worthington, Skilling, Helle and Jackson, and it carries out a truly amazing revolution, or perhaps counter-revolution. The Seattle firm has already built a modest forerunner, the thirteen-story IBM Building in Pittsburgh, on the new principle, which calls for bearing walls—a return to the ancient method of the earliest masonry buildings before Joseph Paxton and Major Jenney changed everything, but these bearing walls are steel. The World Trade center towers will have walls of closely spaced parallel vertical columns of stainless steel. Columns around the elevator core will help to carry the floor loadings, which otherwise will be unsupported and consequently completely free of obstructing columns. Vast amounts of space will be saved, and office layouts will be completely uncluttered by interior structural elements. Fifty thousand people will work in the freely organized spaces.

And the Empire State Building will at long last lose its championship—in height, that is. Would anybody want to make a bet that the World Trade Center will be completed in 1 year and 45 days? As for cost, early estimates, sure to be revised upward, indicated $350 million for the new champion, nine times the cost of the Empire State Building. No question about it, Al Smith had something.

6
A City Solves Its Worst Problem:
The Chicago Sewage System

WHAT IS the most dangerous and stubborn problem cities have had to deal with since their beginnings? Houses and other buildings? No, structures are easy. Streets and transportation? No, traffic snarls and complaints of "strangulation" notwithstanding, transportation troubles are an inconvenience, not a threat to a city's life. Communications, heat, power, medical facilities, police and fire protection? None of these compares with the problem of water.

Water is a two-way essential, and its two different functions are closely interrelated in the engineering life of a city. Water must be brought into the city in enormous quantities in a state fit to be drunk. At the same time, provision must be made to get rid of all the used water, together with all domestic and industrial wastes. The big problem in city after city has been to keep the incoming water clear of the outgoing.

The most catastrophic example of the dilemma, and the most brilliant solution, came from the city of Chicago, which once reversed a river's course and which, more recently, has shown all the cities of the United States and the world a modern blueprint for victory over water pollution.

Every major city is where it is for a good geographical

reason—a natural harbor, a confluence of two rivers, or the point where a river becomes too shallow for ocean ships. Chicago's site is unique. When Louis Joliet and Father Marquette first discovered it in 1673, after lugging their canoes over the Indian portage from the Des Plaines River to the Chicago River, they recognized it as the key to North America. It was the place where the two great water systems met—or almost met. True, it was nothing but a big swampy wilderness, but it was the crossroads of a continent whose fertility was evident enough to any European. It took a while for the vision of Joliet and Marquette to become reality, because there was a good deal of empty space between the Atlantic Coast and Lake Michigan. But 149 years after the journey of the intrepid Frenchmen, the United States Congress authorized the new state of Illinois to erase the "almost" by digging a canal from the Chicago to the Des Plaines rivers, linking the vast watershed of the Mississippi with the Great Lakes. The canal was not begun until 1836 and not completed until 1848, but its promise alone helped get the city of Chicago started. By 1848, there were twenty-eight thousand people living on the shore of Lake Michigan. Twelve years later the population had jumped to one hundred and nine thousand, and with the wealth of the vast American Middle West pouring in, it was clear that the tumultuous growth was going to continue for a long time. Chicago was the great transfer point in an already extensive transportation newtwork, and the steel rails that began to radiate out from it reinforced its position.

Very quickly Chicago began to experience the dangers of too-rapid growth. Like contemporary New York, Boston, London, and Paris, early Chicago relied on shallow wells for its water supply and on outdoor privies for its sewage disposal. Typhoid and dysentery soon gave their grim notice that such farmyard sanitation would not work in a city. A private water company brought clear water from Lake Michigan, peddling it in the streets by cart and bucket. A second company began piping water from the lake. The city government, taking over the enterprise, suddenly found itself up against a massive new threat. The Chicago River carried pollution from the city out into the clear and beautiful Lake Michigan. In 1854, cholera, one of the worst scourges of the era, struck an appalling blow, killing one Chicagoan in every eighteen. The calamity stirred the city into the first of its pioneering efforts in the realm of sanitary engineering. The first integral sewerage system in America and second in the world (that of Hamburg, Germany, in the 1840's being the first), was constructed. However, the new system, though stopping the pollution of the wells, actually complicated the real problem, because it added to the pollution of the Chicago River and Lake Michigan. Much of this came from the waste discarded by the new packing houses, which had sprung up to slaughter the cattle and hogs of the West.

A radical solution was proposed—digging a tunnel far enough out under the lake to reach unpolluted water. The tunneling shield, which would have made the job easy, was soon to be invented, but Chicago couldn't wait. By miraculous luck, the tunnel was successfully completed without it. Yet the growth of the city's industry and population soon pushed the pollution line out to the intake crib, 600 feet from shore. After a rainstorm, Chicago water taps produced a black and greasy liquid nobody dared drink. Another tunnel carried the crib farther out, but once more the city's growth pushed the pollution line out to the crib. A still more radical idea was needed, and a study of the Chicago sanitation and water-supply map suggested a daring move.

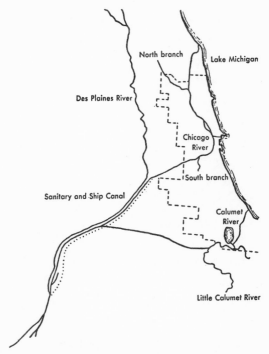

The Chicago problem: how to combine a lake and three rivers into a water supply and sewage system. One solution: to make one river flow the other way, carrying the sewage to the Mississippi rather than to Lake Michigan. But this created problems with other cities along the river.

If the Illinois and Michigan Canal could be made to flow into the Des Plaines River, instead of merely connecting with it, the canal would draw the water of the Chicago River after it, reversing the river's current and making, in effect, Lake Michigan flow to the Mississippi. Automatically, the pollution of the lake front would be ended. This reversal of nature could be accomplished, it appeared, rather easily, merely by deepening the Illinois and Michigan Canal.

In 1865, the canal deepening began. It was finished in 1871, and it worked—for a while. The waters of the Chicago River backed up and slowly retreated through the Canal into the Des Plaines. Then, in 1872, they turned around again and once more began rolling slowly into Lake Michigan. Land promoters had cut a ditch through from the Des Plaines to a branch of the Chicago River to drain a swamp known as Mud Lake, and a heavy flood in 1872 sent a torrent through this ditch, which short-circuited the whole system.

In the meantime, Chicagoans had another problem, for 1871 was the year Mrs. O'Leary's barn caught fire and destroyed 13,500 buildings of the burgeoning metropolis. As a result, nothing could be done immediately about the water problem. A decade later, in 1881–1884, an attempt was made to turn the Chicago River again by means of pumps installed at the juncture of the Illinois and Michigan Canal and the south branch of the river.

It did not work. The pumps were not powerful enough, and the engineeers were still tinkering with the setup when suddenly, on August 2, 1885, nature, which seemed to have it in for Chicago, struck again. It started to rain before dawn; the rain poured down in sheets that turned the sky gray, lashed the streets into mud, and sent torrents into the storm sewers. All day and on through the night it continued, a better than 6-inch fall in 24 hours. The inundation swept through streets, sewers, and catch basins, overwhelming the pumping system and carrying the black scourings of street and sewer out into Lake Michigan, beyond the intake crib of the newest water tunnel. Within days water-borne diseases were epidemic, fatalities mounting.

Once more the embattled "City of Big Shoulders" rolled up its sleeves. A commission was appointed, a quick, thorough study made, and a decision reached that met the problem head on. The plan called for three main steps:

1. Push the Des Plaines River to the west side of its valley to make room for a new canal.
2. Dig a 28-mile canal from the Chicago River at Robey Street (now Damen Avenue) to the Des Plaines at Lockport.
3. Build intercepting sewers along the lake front to carry sewage away from the lake into the new canal.

The new canal, part of whose route lay through solid rock, would decisively reverse the flow of the Chicago River and end the lake-shore pollution forever. By 1889 enabling legislation had passed the legislature, leading to the creation of the Metropolitan Sanitary District of Greater Chicago, with the new plan approved by an overwhelming referendum. No time was lost; there was none to lose. A town of hardly thirty thousand in 1848 when the original Illinois and Michigan Canal was constructed, Chicago now overflowed the plains in every direction with vast warrens of frame houses, brick factories, office buildings, slaughterhouses, steel mills, and railroad yards belonging to a brawling, sprawling population of over a million. Among the crushing mass of newcomers were a tiny handful of older inhabitants who had survived the typhoid-dysentery-cholera plagues and who could remember Chicago as a village.

What was called for was the biggest earth-moving operation ever undertaken on the North American continent. The Suez Canal of a generation earlier had been dug largely by plain hand labor. Along the Des Plaines, the Chicago engineers employed every newest dirt-moving device—steam shovels, steam dredges, drag scrapers, rock drills, and dynamite blasting. They invented new machinery—giant cranes and conveyors—and new techniques. The canal became known as "The American School of Excavation," and its graduates went on to all parts of the country and, in fact, the world—the Panama Canal is an engineering offspring of the Chicago Sanitary and Ship Canal.

From Robey Street (Damen Avenue) to Summit the digging was in good solid earth, but from Summit to Willow Springs the earth was shallow over a rock base, and from Willow Springs on to Lockport the entire canal passed through solid rock. With a bottom width of 160 to 202 feet, the canal was given a slope of 1 foot in 40,000 in the earth sections and 1 in 20,000 through the rock, assuring a capacity of 10,000 cubic feet per second without increasing the current above 2 miles per hour. A swifter current would hamper navigation. The total volume of earth and rock moved was over 40 million cubic yards. This was about two fifths of the volume De Lesseps removed from the 100-mile-long Suez, but De Lesseps was dealing exclusively with soft earth. Chicago's John F. Stevens had to move 12 million cubic yards of solid rock.

For 10 years, the work was relentlessly pushed by machinery, animal power, and men. Eight to ten thousand men worked a 10-hour day, the laborers getting 15 to 17½ cents an hour, with overtime on a straight hourly basis. The skilled workers, boilermakers and stonemasons, were paid

35 to 40 cents an hour, which put them in the upper brackets of United States wage earners of their day.

Earth slides and cave-ins were frequent. In some stretches, layers of a tough, gluey clay stubbornly resisted even the power machinery. But at the end of 1899, the canal was almost holed through. At this point, alarming news suddenly reached Chicago. The State of Missouri was seeking an injunction in federal court to prevent the opening of the canal.

For about fifty years, St. Louis had been eyeing Chicago with the jealous exasperation of an older actress for a young rival who is taking over the top billing. The steamboat had made St. Louis mistress of the Mississippi and metropolis of the West until the Great Lakes and the railroads put Chicago out in front, a position underscored by the brilliant World's Fair of 1893. Now the upstart giant on Lake Michigan was in difficulties as a result of foolishly polluting her own water supply. St. Louis, where people had actually privately applauded the Chicago Fire, could hardly be expected to sympathize with Chicago's water-pollution distress. And at news of the plan to reverse the Chicago River's flow permanently and send Chicago sewage down the Mississippi into St. Louis's drinking water, the reaction was, to say the least, understandable.

Chicago wasn't about to stop digging just because St. Louis objected. On the contrary, the Chicago Board of Trustees moved to speed things up and present the federal courts with a *fait accompli*. A needle dam, a temporary holding dam, was knocked out on January 2, 1900, and water flowed into the new canal channel. Two weeks later, with the top-hatted Board of Trustees precariously crowded onto a mole in front of the dam, the controlling gates at

Lockport were lowered, and the waters from Lake Michigan flowed into the Des Plaines. They swept that sluggish stream along toward the Illinois, pulling the South Branch of the Chicago River and the North Branch from across the city along with them.

St. Louis was beaten, and Chicago's sewage system was legally secure, at least for the time being. The suit of the State of Missouri was dismissed by the Supreme Court in 1906.

In the meantime, the other engineering operations were under way—leading, as it turned out, to even deeper legal waters. The main source of sewage in the Chicago area was precisely along the Lake Michigan water front. Therefore, the big intercepting sewers got next priority after the canal. Laid underground, they were completed by 1907, converging on the North Side of the city at the Lawrence Avenue Pumping Station, on the South Side at the Thirty-Ninth Street Station, superseded later by the Racine Avenue Station. Ranging up to 27 feet in diameter, they were an unheard-of size for their day, built to suffice a city three times the Chicago of 1900. A second canal, the North Shore Channel, was dug parallel to the Lake Michigan shore and ranging from Wilmette on the lake to the North Branch of the river at Lawrence Avenue. Begun in 1908, this channel was completed when the needle dam was knocked out in November 1910.

The last of the three big links in the chain of waters was started the following year. This was the Calumet-Sag Canal, whose function was to do for the exploding population of the South Side what the North Shore Channel did for the North. This was accomplished by connecting the Calumet River with the big canal. This canal, 20 feet deep and

60 wide, required removal of another 13,800,000 cubic yards, including 3½ million of rock. Like the Main Channel, the Calumet-Sag immediately became an important shipway as well as a drainage canal (so important that in 1955, nearly half a century later, Congress voted an appropriation to widen it to 224 feet to accommodate the jump in traffic flowing in from the St. Lawrence Seaway).

Now the whole system was working. Water from the lake was flowing slowly into the North Shore Channel, the Chicago River, and the Calumet River and thence by way of the Sanitary and Ship Canal into the Des Plaines, on into the Illinois, and down to the Mississippi.

And Chicago was in trouble with neighbors on every side.

On the one hand, St. Louis was joined by other towns and cities along the Illinois and Misssissippi charging pollution of their drinking water. On the other hand, Chicago's sister Great Lakes cities claimed the drain-off from Lake Michigan was threatening the level of the whole vast inland-sea chain. The Secretary of War, whose fiat decided the rate of flow permitted in United States canals, was pressured by these cities to cut down the flow. At the same time, Chicago's population passed the two-million mark in 1910 and presented its sanitary engineers with the prospect of a new crisis. What Chicago needed was a higher rate of flow. The Secretary of War turned that idea down, and when the Chicago Sanitary District threatened to take more water from the lake anyway, the War Department filed suit. The legal machinery ground away at the case for several years, and it was not until 1923, a decade and a world war later, that a federal court handed down a decision sustaining the War Department.

By this time, another problem had pushed into the foreground. The city's growth in population was at last slowing down a bit, but a factor little considered back in the cholera-terror days, the waste produced by the city's industry, was rivaling domestic waste in volume:

	1910	1920	1925
Population	2,300,000	3,000,000	3,400,000
Industrial waste in terms of equivalent human population	2,000,000	2,500,000	2,800,000
Total	4,300,000	5,500,000	6,200,000

A twentieth-century city requires a radically different sewage-flow formula from that of a nineteenth-century city. More than ever, Chicago needed a far greater volume of flow in its canal, which of course meant a far heavier drain on the Great Lakes. But not only were the courts sustaining the Secretary of War's refusal to increase the flow, they were also looking sympathetically on a powerful new move to cut it down. This, of course, came from the other Great Lakes cities, now banding together for a legal battle aimed at shutting off completely the alleged loss of water.

The cities seemed to have a point. The level of the Great Lakes was indisputably going down, causing problems all around their busy edges. Recreation areas were disappearing, and what was worse, docks were rising too high above water to unload the long, low lake freighters. By this time, enough was known about the behavior of the lakes, and water in general, to develop a picture of a cycle of high and low water levels. The Great Lakes were known to rise and fall some 6 feet over a period of years.

Next, an international angle was added. With less water

going over Niagara Falls, and a consequent diminution of power, the government of Canada, which shared Niagara power by Canadian–United States treaty, protested to Washington.

The Secretary of War who had originally authorized the diversion of lake water was Elihu Root, a member of Theodore Roosevelt's cabinet in 1901. In 1909, Root was Secretary of State in Taft's cabinet when the Boundary Water Treaty with Canada was negotiated. Naturally, well aware of Chicago's diversion, Root insisted that Lake Michigan, lying wholly inside the borders of the United States, should be excluded from the treaty. The treaty as signed therefore made no mention of the diversion. This gave Chicago's lawyers some ground to fight on, but not much.

Inevitably, the many-sided legal battle mounted toward the Supreme Court. In 1925, the Court upheld the ruling of the federal court, which had sustained the Secretary of War's fiat. This would have had the effect of immediately cutting Chicago's water diversion in half, because the city was actually taking about twice as much water as Root had given permission for in 1901, but simultaneously, the War Department issued a new permit raising the diversion to 8,500 cubic feet per second, about the volume actually being diverted. More outcries came from the Great Lakes cities and Canada.

Represented by their states (Wisconsin, Minnesota, Ohio, Pennsylvania, Michigan, and New York), the cities filed actions in the Supreme Court in 1922, 1925, and 1926. The Supreme Court appointed Charles Evans Hughes, a former Governor of New York and Secretary of State, and a future Chief Justice, as Special Master to hear the combined suits. Hughes conducted exhaustive hearings, listening to reports from lawyers, engineers, and scientists, and finally decided:

1. That as a matter of *fact*, the Chicago diversion was lowering the level of the Great Lakes (by about six inches for 10,000 cubic feet per second) and
2. That as a matter of *law*, the 1925 ruling of the Secretary of War was perfectly valid—Chicago could keep right on diverting.

The argument was not allowed to rest there much more than overnight. The Supreme Court promptly reviewed Special Master Hughes' findings and reversed him on the matter of law. Chicago was ordered to stop taking water from Lake Michigan. To implement the decision, the Court directed Hughes to provide a plan for a graduated reduction of Chicago water diversion. Hughes reported back in 1930 with a recommendation that the cut be accomplished in three stages and that by 1938 the city get down to the maximum permitted by the Court, a diversion of 1,500 cubic feet per second, barely enough to keep the canal water moving.

In framing his plan, Hughes had the collaboration of Chicago's sanitary engineers. During the twenty years the lawyers had been arguing, the engineers had not been asleep. As far back as 1909, George M. Wisner, then chief engineer, had inaugurated a program of experimentation to find a treatment system for disposal of wastes. In this, Wisner had the backing of Colonel Robert R. McCormick, future publisher of *The Chicago Tribune*, then president of the Board of the Metropolitan District. Just after World War I the Wisner-McCormick research program resulted in the construction of a small but history-making treatment plant at Maywood. Made to serve a local population of about forty thousand, the little Maywood plant was designed to test new and sophisticated sewage-treatment techniques, especially the *activated-sludge* process.

Two separate problems are involved in a sewage system, it should be observed: storm-water and domestic sewage. The old Roman and medieval European systems were strictly for storm-water disposal, to prevent flooding of the narrow city streets. In *Les Misérables*, Jean Valjean carries his wounded friend Marius to safety through a storm sewer. Domestic sewage in Victor Hugo's Paris was removed from the city by wagoners. It was not until cities grew so densely populated that outdoor privies and wagoners could not cope with the problem that domestic sewage systems came into being. Some cities built whole new networks of conduits to carry the domestic sewage; others simply enlarged their existing storm sewers into "combined systems."

The long debate over the two systems is not without interest for laymen. A combined system is cheaper. But domestic (and industrial-waste) sewage flow is very steady, while storm flow on the other hand is extremely erratic, sometimes running fifty to one hundred times the domestic flow. Therefore, a combined sewer must be built to carry a small depth of flow in dry weather, but to be capable of suddenly accepting a very large flow. Since the treatment plants cannot begin to take the storm flow (they are designed to handle up to double the dry-weather flow), it follows that every time it rains hard much of the combined flow must be routed straight into the waterways, carrying sewage with it. This of course is pollution. On the other hand, storm water flushed from city streets into a separate conduit system is itself polluted. Further, according to an expert authority, "it seems almost impossible to prevent illegal sanitary sewer connections into separate storm sewers." While Chicago's experience with the dual system seems to indicate an advantage for separation, the question is still not closed.

Although Chicago was the second city in the world to pioneer a sewage-disposal system, its system, like all those of the nineteenth century, consisted merely of moving the sewage out of town. For a city like New York or London, situated on the ocean, this was a good expedient for a long time, but Chicago, situated on a fresh-water lake and a fresh-water river system, was facing squarely for the first time the real sanitation problem of a modern city—how to render all domestic and industrial waste completely innocuous.

The Sanitary and Ship Canal had trained a generation of excavating engineers. The new job trained a generation of sanitary engineers. Scores of leading members of the profession served the vital project that had been begun by the foresighted George Wisner. The importance of the problem is underlined by the fact that one of Wisner's successors as Chief Engineer of the Sanitary District, Edward J. Kelly, was later elected Mayor of Chicago.

The treatment method as finally worked out consists of a series of steps: coarse screening to remove large objects that would clog mechanisms or pipe lines; grit chambers to settle out sand, cinders, and so on; primary settling tanks to remove heavy organic solids; aeration tanks, where the mixture of raw sewage and returned activated sludge is aerated by air diffused in fine bubbles near the bottom of the tanks; and settling tanks, where practically all of the suspended solids are removed from the mixture.

In the final step, the treated effluent flows into the canal. The removed solids, called *sludge* while still in a fluid state, are disposed of by one of three processes: digestion and incorporating in fill; vacuum filtering and heat drying (flash drying) for sale as fertilizer; or wet oxidation (the Zimmermann process) with disposal of the ash in lagoons and retreatment of the liquid in the plant. The Chicago Sanitary District uses all three of these methods, and is researching better ones.

Development of the full, many-step process began at the little experimental Maywood plant and continued through the giant Calumet and Stickney plants. The first great stride was the activated-sludge process, the principle of which had been discovered by British chemists just before World War I. Chicago's sanitary engineers seized on it and, working around the clock at the same time as engineers in nearby Milwaukee and in England, turned it into a practical and extremely valuable technique. *Activated sludge* is sewage sludge rich in bacteria. Seeded into incoming sewage and agitated in the presence of an ample air supply, it causes rapid oxidation of organic matter. The result is removal of about 95 percent of all bacteria, and more than 90 percent of all organic matter.

In 1925, the chemist John A. Palmer, working with F. W. Mohlman, made an important improvement in chemical precipitation possible with his discovery that ferric chloride made an excellent coagulant prior to vacuum filtering. This was of great importance in dewatering the enormous quantity of organic solids removed by the treatment works.

A few years later Chief Engineer Philip Harrington and Chief Mechanical Engineer William A. Dundas developed another important technique, *flash drying*. This is a means of converting sludge into a material suitable for fertilizer

by disintegrating the wet sludge cake with a burst of super-
heated vapor. In a 90-second trip through a duct system,
the sludge is dried and then separated from the gas in
which it is suspended by "cyclone" blowers.

The methods developed in the Maywood plant were first
put into large-scale use in the huge Calumet Treatment
Plant, completed in 1922. The even bigger North Side
Works was finished in 1928, and the West Side Works, in
1931, but the city was still growing, up from three to four
million in population, and in the 1930's Chicago built the
treatment plant that won the "Seventh Wonder" accolade
from the American Society of Civil Engineers. This was the
Southwest Treatment Plant, which was combined with the
West Side Works to form the Stickney Plant—by far the
largest in the world, combining all the new techniques on
the biggest scale. (Chicago's second-largest plant, the
North Side Works, is probably also the world's second-
biggest, which gives an idea of the remarkable magnitude
of Chicago's effort in water-pollution control.) The effluent
from the vast Stickney Plant emerges as a clear, odorless
liquid, which may safely be pumped into the Sanitary and
Ship Canal. The remaining impurities are microscopic particles in suspension. The sludge, after being dosed with
ferric chloride, filtered, and flash-dried at 1,300 degrees
Fahrenheit by a combination of sludge vapor and combus-
tion gas, emerges as an excellent organic fertilizer, free of
harmful bacteria. The Stickney Plant produces 500 tons of
it a day, and the Sanitary District sells more than $2 mil-
lion worth a year.

However, the market for fertilizer could not take all the
Chicago sludge, and still another technique had to be developed to get rid of the remainder at low cost. An engi-

neer, F. J. Zimmermann, came up with a method of burning the wastes in a 400- to 700-degree heat under pressure.
The heat generated helps sustain the reaction and also produces electricity. The products are a fine, inert ash that is
completely inoffensive, and water. Following successful
testing in a pilot plant, the Sanitary District has built four
50-ton units to employ the Zimmermann process at its
Stickney Plant. Together with its network of big intercepting sewers, the four big treatment plants virtually solved
the 100-year-old Chicago sewage problem as far as domestic and industrial wastes were concerned, but the other part
of the problem—storm water—gave the city major head-
aches in the 1950's. In 1954, a heavy rainstorm caused $25
million worth of damage to business establishments alone,
and, in 1957, another hit just as hard. The trouble was that
the sewer mains, drainage ditches, and small streams that
carried storm water to the Sanitary and Ship Canal and the
Des Plaines River could be locally overpowered by an intensive rainfall, while Joliet, where the canal and river
join, forms a major bottleneck in a big storm.

The Sanitary District attacked this problem by dredging
the North Shore Channel, the Des Plaines bed, and various
tributary streams deeper and by developing a master plan
for the future. Profiting from the experience of the past, the
master plan looks ahead no less than 50 years. The core of
it is the construction of a number of flood reservoirs,
mostly of the pumped-storage type, along the upper
reaches of the rivers and streams. Together with widening
and deepening of channels and other improvements, the
program may cost as much as $200 million—"almost as
much as the damage caused by one flood," comments one
engineer. Here, too, Chicago is pioneering.

Thus there have been three battles in the Chicago sanitation war: first, the lake-pollution struggle, ending victoriously with the reversal of flow of the Chicago and Calumet rivers. Second, the sewage-treatment battle, triumphantly concluded by the completion of the Stickney Plant. Third, the fight now going on against the storm waters.

It is a war with no armistice, according to Norval Anderson, who retired in 1964 as Chief Engineer of the Sanitary District. Anderson's 44-year career has virtually spanned the whole history of Chicago's sewage-treatment struggle. Probably the only civil engineer in the United States who plays polo and rides to hounds, Anderson started out working at the Maywood Plant in 1921 and has helped design and build all the big treatment plants, notably the Stickney. As Chief Engineer of the District, he outlined the pumped-storage-reservoir solution to the storm-water problem.

In Anderson's view, there is no such thing as a final solution. Quite apart from the fact that the lake states are again trying to get the Supreme Court to cut down Chicago's diversion-flow allotment, the city's metropolitan growth in people and industry continues. Some $25 million a year will be spent up to and beyond the year 2000 for intercepting sewers and new treatment facilities. From 10 to 20 miles of intercepting sewers are being built in the Sanitary District every year. The North Side Works, expanded in 1937, was enlarged again in 1962 by one third of capacity. The Calumet Works is completing a similar enlargement. The Stickney is undergoing an expansion proportionally similar, that is, by one third, but far bigger because of its size. Various lesser constructions are also under way or scheduled.

The information accumulated by Chicago engineers is al-

ready proving invaluable elsewhere. Such inland cities as
Detroit, St. Louis, and Kansas City, dependent throughout
their history on pollution dilution, are busily studying total
treatment; today, let alone in the years ahead, dilution just
isn't safe. And the big coastal metropolises—New York,
Philadelphia, and Los Angeles—are discovering that dumping in the ocean will not work any more either. New York
has been ordered by the Interstate Sanitation Commission
to stop dumping its one-half billion gallons of sewage per
day into the Hudson and East rivers.

In the next third of a century, every major American
city, and cities in the industrially advanced countries
everywhere, will accept the lesson that, regardless of local
geography, the only answer to the sewage problem is complete purification.

7

Carrying a River Over the Mountains: Oroville, California

CALIFORNIA, as many Californians have told Easterners, has everything. The trouble is, it doesn't have it all in the right places. Climate, soil, mineral resources, and ocean shore make southern California a great place to live and work, so that over three quarters of the expanding population of this largest state are concentrated in the southern half, with an especially dense cluster around Los Angeles in the extreme south. They have everything, with one exception: water. Over three quarters of the state's plentiful volume of fresh water flows in the sparsely settled, mountainous, forested northern half, 400 to 800 miles away.

Transporting water over long distances is one of engineering's oldest problems. The Romans did it with tunnels and aqueducts all over Italy, Spain, Gaul, and the rest of their empire. One of their tunnels, 15 miles long, serves the city of Athens today; another keeps the Fontana di Trevi flowing. Yet even Roman engineers would be staggered by the size of California's problem. In the first place, today's United States citizen uses far more water than did a Roman for domestic purposes—washing, cooking, plumbing, heating, cooling use up to 150 gallons a day. Also, the demands of irrigation, while by no means unknown to Roman engineers, were on a much more modest scale in Augustan Italy than those of the huge, high-yield farm lands of the San Joaquin Valley. Finally, modern industry has created a tremendous water demand wholly unknown in earlier times. Los Angeles's oil refineries need 400 barrels of water to process 1 barrel of crude oil. A ton of steel is cooled by 100,000 gallons of water. A simple case of lima beans uses 250 gallons.

Fifty years ago, Los Angeles was already reaching east into the Owens Valley to pipe water to what was then a city of two hundred and fifty thousand. Not long after, in the 1920's, San Francisco built its Hetch Hetchy project. Oakland and the other East Bay cities crossed the San Joaquin Valley to get water from the Mokelumne River. In the 1930's, the federal government contributed to development of the vast Central Valley Project, embodying flood control, irrigation, and water supply. Though the Central Valley scheme was fully adequate for a state with a population of six million, it was obviously not going to take care of the problem of a state twice that size. Los Angeles and twelve sister cities banded together to form the Metropolitan Water District and build the biggest aqueduct ever undertaken, stretching all the way to the Colorado River, 240 miles away. This massive work, carried out in 7 years, embracing canals, tunnels, pumping plants, reservoirs, and a major dam (Parker), at a cost of $220 million, was another of the "Seven Wonders of the Modern World" named by the American Society of Civil Engineers in 1955. It also stirred a good deal of attention in nonengineering circles. In fact, like the Chicago Sanitation and Ship Canal, it started a real legal battle. The Colorado River rises at the Continental Divide and flows southwest through three states—Colorado, Arizona, and California. The lower stretch of the river, the most valuable part, lies mostly in Arizona, but part of it forms the Arizona-California border. When California began dipping into the big river with both hands with the new aqueduct, Arizona got alarmed and sued. After several years of battling, the Supreme Court divided up the river this way:

California	4.4 million acre-feet a year
Arizona	2.8 million acre-feet a year
Nevada	.3 million acre-feet a year

An *acre-foot* is 1 acre of water 1 foot deep and retails in southern California for $20. The Court's arithmetic adds up to 7.5 million acre-feet, the volume the Colorado usually supplies. When it does not, everybody will get cut down on a pro-rata basis, but before the decision, California was taking 5.1 million acre-feet, and was looking forward to raising its intake to around 5.4 million. Thus the decision was a bad one for California, though it was not totally unexpected. Like Chicago in a similar crisis, California had already been trying to find a solution. If anything, the California problem was even more complicated because of the divergent local interests inside the state. The difficulty of reconciling these was such that nothing but the overwhelming urgency of the problem could ever have supported the interminable wrangle in the state legislature, which Governor Pat Brown at last succeeded in resolving.

There was actually enough water in the state to take California into the twenty-first century, but setting aside the engineering problem, there were such matters as this: If you plan a water-supply system to take from water-rich counties and give to water-starved counties, you run the risk of ending up in twenty or thirty years with a painfully ironic situation—the sparsely settled water-rich counties have filled up and now need water that is being piped through elaborate aqueducts and pumping stations to some place 500 miles away. This has already happened in California, and the outcry has been loud. It is called the "county-of-origin problem," and is one of many that had to be solved.

What was required, very evidently, was a master plan that would encompass, as fully as human ingenuity could, all the political, economic, and engineering problems of water supply for the next sixty or seventy years. The year 2020 was taken as a target date. "Pronounced twenty-twenty that means perfect vision, and we haven't quite got that, but we've done our best," said William E. Warne, director of the State Water Resources Board. The giant blueprint, known as the California Water Plan, was originally drawn up in 1957, while the Supreme Court's decision on the Colorado River was still impending. Studies made after the decision have revealed that because of a special dispensation granted the Phoenix-Tucson district of Arizona, California's share of the Colorado water will begin falling substantially below the 4.4 million acre-feet figure by 1975. The California Water Plan was immediately revised and its implementation given a fresh urgency.

The engineers studied the map of the state mile by mile and then went out and examined nearly every foot of it. They measured every river and tributary on the northern California coast and tramped all its meadows. How much water was flowing out to sea? How much was in the ground? They earmarked all possible dam sites and figured where tunnels would be required through mountains and foothills. They calculated, finally, that 12 million acre-feet of water could be exported from the northern coast without endangering future local needs and that the export could be carried out on an economically sound basis.

The aim of the California Water Plan is to stop millions of acre-feet of northern California water from being poured uselessly into the Pacific Ocean. Most of this waste takes place at the mouth of the great Sacramento River, a confluence of northern mountain streams that is joined by the San Joaquin coming up from the south and the Mokelumne from the west at a point just east of San Francisco known as the Delta. The heart of the plan is the Feather River Project, designed to tame a turbulent tributary of the Sacramento that up to now has been noted chiefly as a troublemaker and to convert it into the major feeding source for the new California Aqueduct. This is a story in itself, leaving even the heroic-size Colorado Aqueduct far behind. With its Coast Division, a 103-mile branch supplying San Luis Obispo County, this vast trunk line of canals, conduits, tunnels through mountains, pumping stations, dams, and power stations has a total length of 562 miles. This is exclusive of two lesser aqueducts, the North Bay and South Bay, carrying water 60 and 40 miles, respectively, to the Bay area. The main line runs 444 miles from the Delta down to Perris Reservoir in Riverside County, southeast of Los Angeles.

Even Roman aqueducts were complex structures, running sometimes in canals at ground level, sometimes in tunnels below the ground, sometimes above ground in long, lofty bridges (the massive, triple-tiered Pont du Gard, in southern France, biggest bridge of the ancient world, is a Roman aqueduct). A modern aqueduct such as the California has tunnels, horseshoe shaped and as big as two-lane highway tunnels; cut-and-cover conduits built by trenching and covering over with concrete lining; canals, open but with concrete lining; siphons, huge concrete pipes laid on the ground in places where the water must be carried across valleys; pumping stations to lift the water over hills and mountains; and dams to furnish power for the pumping stations. There are also a few other frills, such as desilting plants, with which the Romans did not bother. Finally, the California Aqueduct will have one extremely novel feature —a pair of nuclear reactors. Each capable of producing 500,000 kilowatt hours per year, the reactors will do two things for California's water problem: run the electric pumps for the main 2,000-foot lift over the Tehachapi Mountains, and power a desalinization plant that will convert sea water for use in the immediate region.

The pumps themselves are something new because they must lift 1½ million gallons a minute up that 2,000 feet. That much water has been lifted before in the United States, but never so high; water has been lifted higher than that in Europe, but never in such volume. For combined size and height of lift, this is a record.

At the same time, great care must be taken once the water is over the mountains to keep it from rolling too rapidly through the western slopes on the west side of the San Joaquin Valley. A canal aqueduct must flow, but it must flow slowly—too fast a current and you may have to rebuild the canal.

Finally, a real California problem: in the Tehachapis, the line of the aqueduct cuts squarely across the line of the great San Andreas fault, the biggest earthquake fault in North America and source of the devastating San Francisco quake of 1906, the equally big though less destructive temblors of 1857 and 1940, and several lesser quakes. As

huge blocks of the earth's crust drift northward at an inexorable 2 inches a year, the strains inevitably produce new
earthquakes, and nothing, at least from where science
stands now, can stop them. Therefore, the engineers have
decided to face the threat by simply building their aqueducts on the surface as they cross the San Andreas instead of
tunneling through the mountain. That calls for more pumping, but it is much easier to repair a canal than a tunnel.

The California Water Plan really began moving when
an act of the state legislature in 1959, passed after arduous
struggles with the various local interests, authorized a referendum on a bond issue. State legislatures have authorized bond issues before, but never anything like this:
$1,750,000,000, enough to build the Verrazano-Narrows
Bridge, the English Channel Tunnel, the Tokaido Line, the
Empire State Building, and the Simplon Tunnel all added
together. The bond referendum was on the ballot in the
election of 1960 and, despite its unheard-of size and the
heat of the controversy it engendered, won voter approval.
The California Water Plan, in the active form of the State
Water Project, was in business.

Its business was to wholesale water to local water agen-
cies. These range in size from the Metropolitan Water District of Southern California, the combine that built the Colorado Aqueduct, which contracted for 1.5 million acre-
feet, down to the Littlerock Creek Irrigation District,
which contracted for a modest 2,000 acre-feet. The contracts provide for a gradual growth of service up to the
contractual levels. In 1963, the project was already deliv-
ering the first trickle, 44,000 acre-feet, which by 1970 will
grow to a third of a million acre-feet. The real upsurge will
only come in the next decade with completion of the

Feather River Project. Ultimately, volume will reach 3.5 million acre-feet.

The idea is to tame the wild Feather River and make it produce an even flow, winter and summer, to the Delta,

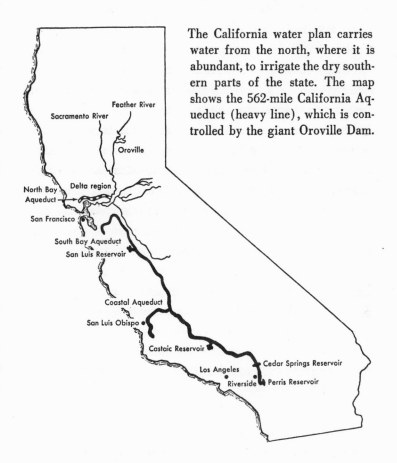

The California water plan carries water from the north, where it is abundant, to irrigate the dry southern parts of the state. The map shows the 562-mile California Aqueduct (heavy line), which is controlled by the giant Oroville Dam.

making this natural pool a sort of "ever normal granary" of water for the two big metropolitan areas, the Bay and Los Angeles.

Its gentle name notwithstanding, the Feather is a boisterous, snow-fed mountain torrent. In years past, it has frequently exploded over its banks and caused large-scale flood damage. Thanks to the river's delinquency record, California is getting financial help from the federal government, which will contribute 22 percent of the total cost as part of the federal flood-control program. Most of the dam's $440 million price, however, will come out of the bond issue, to be paid for largely by the water purchasers.

To take this brawling river by the scruff of the neck and make it deliver an even, easy-to-handle volume of water every year, two outsize weapons are needed—a very big dam and a very big reservoir. There have been relocation problems at Oroville, not to mention along the right-of-way of the California Aqueduct, but in this thinly settled rugged country, there was still enough room for an artificial lake with a surface of 15,500 acres and a 167-mile shoreline. It will hold 3.5 million acre-feet of water, or five times the yearly volume lost in the Supreme Court division of the Colorado River.

Aqueduct, pumping stations, reservoir—these bring us to the heart of the business, the dam itself. Building dams is certainly nothing new, as the ruins of an ancient Egyptian dam in the Wadi Gerrawi attest. The Romans constructed many, and stimulated dam building with the invention of the water wheel. Medieval Europe was covered with little dams, whose millraces and waterwheels ground grain, sawed wood, even operated forge hammers. Then in progressive sixteenth-century Spain, the large dam made its comeback. To tame some of their roaring mountain rivers, Spanish engineers of Cervantes' day built solid-masonry dams over a hundred feet high of a nearly rectangular cross section.

Big dams continued to be built on this design, though not very often, till the mid-nineteenth century. The French engineers made an important discovery. Demonstrating that the solid "gravity" dams resisted the pressure of their streams solely by their weight, they devised a way to save material with a more efficiently designed profile. British engineers used the new French design on a large scale for major dams in India, and when Sir Benjamin Baker and a team of British and Indian engineers built the first Aswan Dam at the turn of the century, it ranked as one of the world's largest, though only 96 feet high. The era of high dams was suddenly born with the decision of the United States government under Theodore Roosevelt to go in for reclamation on a large scale. The Roosevelt Dam on the Salt River, Arizona, built in 1905–1911, rose in a sweeping curve of massive-stone wall, resembling a medieval castle, to a height of 280 feet from bedrock. The Arrowrock Dam, completed in 1916 over the Boise River in Idaho, carried the record to 350 feet.

Height, however, is only one way of measuring a dam's size, and not the most important way. The Arrowrock and later dams built to block the narrow gorges of America's western rivers are designed on a special principle, the engineers taking advantage of the solid canyon walls to anchor what amounts to an arch laid on its face, the open end toward the flood. The highest dam of this type in the United States is the 730-foot Hoover.

To block a river running through a broad valley a much larger dam is required, and for this purpose the *earth-fill dam* with an impermeable core was developed. As a big dam, it was pioneered in the United States by the Green

Mountain Dam over a Colorado River tributary which was completed in 1943. A solid block with earth or earth-and-rock fill requires a much thicker barrier than reinforced concrete, but fill is so much cheaper than masonry that the total cost is less. There is another way to cut down the cost of a dam—use better rather than cheaper materials, and make the dam a very thin arch. American and French engineers have tried this method, notably at Stevenson's Creek in the United States and Le Gage in France. Still another possibility is the *hollow masonry* gravity dam, in which masonry facing is used to reduce the needed amount of earth fill.

Still, the earth-fill, or embankment, dam remains the tried-and-true block for broad streams. Such a dam is essentially a symmetrically shaped submerged mountain. The mountain is composed of specialized layers and segments of different kinds of material, organized into a pattern precisely calculated to stop the flow of water with maximum certainty at minimum expense. Simply to dump an enormous amount of rock fill in the river would hardly serve. Water would seep underneath as well as through such a mass.

The *grout* (liquid cement) *curtain* runs down to bed-

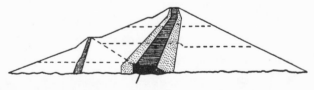

The Oroville Dam is a mountainlike construction of earth fill with impervious sections to keep water from seeping through. Above, a cross-sectional sketch of the pervious (white), transition (dotted), and impervious (horizontal bars). Core block and grout curtain, black.

rock, effectively shutting off any flow of water underneath the mountain. The core block and impervious segment above it stop the water from flowing through. The pervious segments, forming the main bulk of the dam, protect the impervious center.

This is a fairly standard design, similar to those of the Fort Peck and Oahe dams on the upper Missouri, the world's two largest embankment dams. Oroville, with 78 million cubic yards of fill, is a little smaller than the big Missouri barriers, and even a trifle smaller than its contemporary California sister, the San Luis. Its height record, 747.5 feet, 20.5 feet higher than the Hoover, is certainly remarkable for an earth-fill dam, but it is surpassed by various concrete arches built or under construction. The Russians have two 990-foot-high dams now under construction. Where Oroville stands head and shoulders above all rivals is as an earth-moving job. The "borrow area" at Oroville, from which the material must be transported to the dam site, stretches from 7 to 13 miles away. Oroville engineers think their job breaks the previous record in ton-miles of earth moving by about 1,000 percent.

Because the contract was awarded to the lowest bidder, the winning contractor, Oro Dam Constructors, a combine of seven major firms, had to figure closely, which in a job of this size demands a fair amount of figuring. An embankment dam is built in sections year by year, with each year's fill so placed as to keep the dam always protected against flood. First, a core block of concrete is planted in the river. Oroville's core block is a stout 231,600 cubic yards. Against this solid core, a *cofferdam* is erected, whose function is to hold the river out of the channel, forcing it to detour around the site of the main construction. The cofferdam at Oroville is a very sizable dam itself, 400 feet high and containing an impervious core. It becomes the forward slope of the main dam.

However, the big problem is moving the earth. To make good on their contract, the Oro Dam constructors had to devise some quite new techniques as well as make a maximum use of already known ones. One of the joint venturers, by no coincidence, happens to own the McDowell-Wellman Company of Cleveland, which is a specialist in making heavy industrial equipment. Much of the machinery seen at Oroville is of a type not usually used by the construction industry but imported from mining and bulk-material-handling fields. Giant crawler-mounted transfer conveyors, self-propelled traveling hopper cars, and above all a stupendous gadget known as a digging wheel, make the Oroville operation a model of United States engineering—highly mechanized, highly efficient, highly cost and time conscious.

Building the Oroville Dam required moving tremendous amounts of rock and dirt—up to 4,200 cubic yards per hour. To do this a wheel excavator (left) transferred earth to conveyers, which dumped it on 10-car trains. The trains moved the material to a dumping station 12 miles across the river. Conveyor belts then moved it through the reclaim tunnel to distribution conveyors, truck-loading hoppers, and finally to the dam.

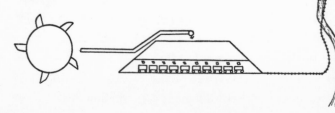

The fastest railroad. Evidence that railroads are not dead, the Tokaido Line speeds through the Japanese countryside at 125 mph. Except for starting and stopping, the trains run on automatic train control. Passenger trains operate during daylight hours only; freight trains, at night. *Japanese National Railways*

The longest tunnel. A mile below the top of the mountain, tunneling crews faced floods, cave-ins, and temperatures of more than 120 degrees Fahrenheit. But the tunnel they built, the Simplon, provided a vital link between Italy and Switzerland. *Swiss National Tourist Office*

Something new on the sea. The first nuclear-powered merchant ship, the N.S. *Savannah*, was launched at Camden, New Jersey, in July 1959. The ship, 596 feet long, derives its power from a pressurized water reactor. *Babcock & Wilcox*

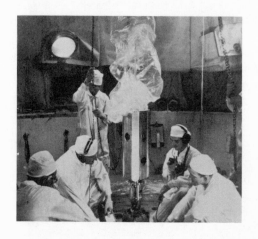

A practice fuel loading on board the N.S. *Savannah*. The fuel element being lowered into the reactor compartment is covered with a nylon shroud to protect it from dirt and other contamination.

Babcock & Wilcox

Cable spinning on the Verrazano-Narrows Bridge. The strands were drawn by a wheel over the near tower, down and across the span, up and over the far tower, and down to the anchorage on the other side. The wheel was 48 inches in diameter and made its trip across the water and back in less than twelve minutes.

United States Steel Corporation

The longest bridge. Spanning the harbor between Brooklyn and Staten Island, the Verrazano-Narrows Bridge stretches 4,260 feet from tower to tower. Its Brooklyn tower is 860 feet over-all, as high as an eighty-story skyscraper. *United States Steel Corporation*

The tallest building. Towering above the lights of Fifth Avenue, the Empire State Building rose high above its midtown neighbors in 1931. At the time of this picture, the original eighty-six stories had been completed. The new sixteen-story observation deck was under construction. *Lewis W. Hine*

Few buildings are completed ahead of schedule and at less than estimated cost. Yet the Empire State was rushed to a record finish in one year and forty-five days, and the $50 million cost estimate had to be revised downward—the completed project, including site, demolition, and construction, came to less than $41 million.

Lewis W. Hine

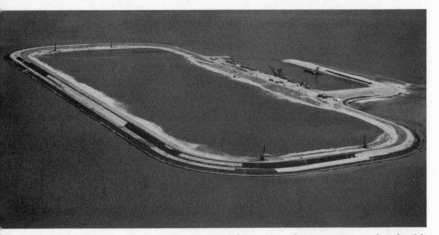

Holding back the sea. This massive ring dike provides protection for building the Haringvliet Dam, one of the major barriers in the Dutch Delta Project. The largest cofferdam ever built, it is 4,500 feet long and 27 feet high on the side that faces the sea. *Netherlands Information Service*

Supplying water where it is needed. California, a fast-growing state that has its water in the north and population in the south, is bringing the two together by a 500-mile network of canals, conduits, and tunnels. Heart of the project is the 746-foot Oroville Dam, which will hold back the rivers of the north and prevent them from flowing into the sea. *California Department of Water Resources*

LEFT: The Aswan tames the Nile. Before the actual High Dam is built, cofferdams such as this one will divert the river around the site. Behind the new dam will be a 300-mile lake; in front of it, Egypt will have a steady flow of water for irrigation and power.

Hamilton Wright

RIGHT: Abu Simbel in November 1963. The cofferdam to hold back the Nile is nearing completion in the background. *Hamilton Wright*

Wonders of the thirteenth century B.C. These four statues of Ramses II, each 67 feet tall, stand guard before the temple at Abu Simbel. Because the new dam will flood their location, the entire temple will be cut out of the mountain and reset on higher ground. *UNESCO/Laurenza*

Dismantling at Abu Simbel.
The artist's sketch shows
how the temple will be
moved to a new site above
the water level of Lake
Nasser. The Nile, at its
present level, is in the foreground.   *V. B. B.*

Hell Hole: the Titan Missile base near Denver, Colorado. The silos extended an additional 125 feet below these excavations and were connected by under ground tunnels. After it was built, the site was covered with a deep layer o earth. Only the access areas remained visible.   *United States Air Force*

A voice in the sky. This 380-ton horn antenna swivels both vertically and hori zontally to track the Early Bird satellite. From the earth station at Andover Maine, the horn picks up and transmits signals between Europe and North America.   *American Telephone and Telegraph*

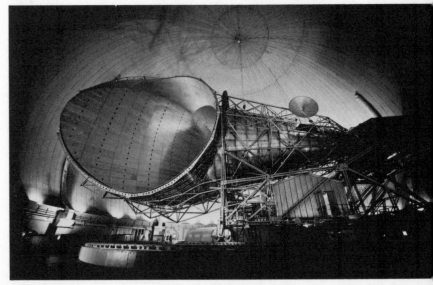

The minutest details were worked out in advance. A reclaim tunnel was built under the storage pile so that the loading trains on the service track could be automatically filled ten at a time. A string of forty cars can be loaded in the incredible time of 14 minutes.

The impervious-core material, to be dumped on top of the concrete core block, was excavated in the early stages by large draglines, later by the digging wheel, a 668-ton self-propelled monster 100 feet long, 44 feet wide, and 45 feet high. Going full speed, the 30-foot wheel's furiously spinning curved buckets, each with a 1.8 cubic-yard capacity, can claw out 4,200 cubic yards of earth and rock per hour. Whirling at a slightly more moderate pace, it can dig 3,500 cubic yards an hour around the clock. "The key piece of equipment on the job," said William Warne. It deposits the material in truck-loading hoppers, which are instantly hauled away by Athey wagons, gigantic trailers taking 100 tons at a time. Tractors do the pulling to a big hopper feeding a conveyor belt running into the train station.

As for the pervious material that forms the main bulk of the dam, its handling is almost completely automated. A 7,000-foot conveyor belt carries it directly to the train station as the excavator digs it out. The excavator starts its work close to the train station and gradually moves farther and farther away until the belt extends to its extreme length. When everything has been dug up for 7,000 feet around the train station, the station is picked up and moved.

Three forty-car trains, pulled by twin 2,500-horsepower Diesel electric engines, keep the loading-moving-unloading cycle going continuously. At the dam site, two of the machines supplied by the Wellman Company take over from the Diesels. An automatic train pusher lines up the forty-car string, and a car dumper grabs the steel gondolas, two at a time, and tilts them; the cars have rotary couplings so that the tilting doesn't uncouple them. The double dumping takes just 38 seconds and lands the material in a concrete hopper feeding a broad, 96-inch conveyor belt that carries it across the river. There, more automatic equipment unloads, stores, sorts out, mixes appropriately, and carries the final material to the proper point along the embankment, where it is packed down by four runs of a 100-ton pneumatic compactor.

Even a superautomated operation such as this one can get in trouble with a river as unpredictable as the Feather. The main dam construction has been protected by diversion of the river through a 35-foot-bore, nearly 1-mile-long diversion tunnel, but installations downstream were considered safe. In October of 1963, an out-of-season flood swept away a Bailey drawbridge, flooded the heading of one of the two diversion tunnels under construction, and did sundry other damage. The contractors hardly got things in shape again when another flood hit in January, with the water rising 50 feet in 48 hours. The second Bailey bridge was knocked off its hinge, though not lost completely this time. The contractor who owned the Bailey bridge hastily threw up a timber-cribbing stockade.

The same contractor, Frazier-Davis Construction Company, had a downstream cofferdam damaged. Thereby hangs an interesting aspect of Oroville and of the whole State Water Project.

The main idea of the plan is, of course, to supply water where it is needed, the main idea behind most dams. In addition, there is the flood-control value, which led the federal government to contribute one fifth of the Oroville cost. Also, keeping the Sacramento River's flow even will save a wide belt of good farm land from being periodically ruined by salinity when the returning water brings the ocean in with it. Then there is power; build a dam for any purpose and you can, if you want it, get electrical power. If you want to move the water a long way, you need the power for the pumping stations. About half of the power supply for the California Aqueduct will come from project power plants—Oroville and its subsidiary, the Thermalito, generate 2.5 billion kilowatt hours—the rest from power-recovery plants along the way and from the nuclear reactor.

Aside from water, flood control, and power, a dam can do some very important things. The Frazier-Davis cofferdam the flood hit was around a new fish hatchery. One of the things California has learned to think about in connection with water relocation is fish and wildlife. Disturb a marsh where ducks breed, and it must be replaced. Take away the spawning ground of salmon and steelhead, and if the fish are to survive, another one must be provided. Otherwise a valuable natural resource is lost. Therefore, the State Water Project includes provisions for protection of fish and wildlife in all affected areas. This is what the Frazier-Davis cofferdam was for.

Another value of a dam: recreation. The lake above the Oroville Dam is perfectly good for swimming, boating, and fishing. It is not a baldly geometric and synthetic lake but a completely natural one, with fingers extending into picturesque canyons around its periphery. Public parks will dot its shores as they do those of the other big new state reservoirs.

The five small upstream dams in the Feather River project and in the San Joaquin Valley will also contribute important recreation facilities. These satellites of the Oroville Dam will give Californians and visitors areas to fish and swim along the Westside Freeway, which for many miles parallels the Aqueduct line.

The project, with its interlocking aims, will be completed in the decade 1961–1971. During its course, another considerably broader "water decade" will get started. This is the International Hydrological Decade, sponsored by UNESCO, whose purpose will be to launch a worldwide search for new sources of water. Taken along with such political developments as the United States–Soviet joint research on atomic-powered desalinization, this is a clear signpost of the future. Water is going to be a problem, and not just in California. What California learns from its own work will benefit dozens of nations over the next century.

8
Driving Back the Sea:
The Dutch Delta

"An unfortunate land flooded twice every twenty-four hours, forcing the inhabitants to live on man-made hills where they build huts in which they warm their limbs, stiffened by northerly winds, beside a blazing fire."

PLINY'S DESCRIPTION OF THE NETHERLANDERS,
FIRST CENTURY A.D.

"Een volk dat leeft, bouwt aan zijn toekomst." (*A vigorous nation builds for its future.*)

MOTTO ON THE BARRIER DAM MONUMENT

IF EGYPT is the gift of the Nile, the Netherlands is a theft from the ocean. It is an ingenious and spirited piece of thievery that has been going on for centuries and that is today reaching a climax in the vastest single engineering effort of the twentieth century. The huge tidal delta formed by the outpouring of the Rhine, Maas, and Scheldt Rivers, and the corresponding tremendous influx of tidal ocean water through this open gate in the coastline, is slowly, firmly, inexorably being closed. The result, to be achieved by 1980, will be a huge fresh-water lake, 30,000 acres of newly created farm land, an invaluable industrial area, and miles of parks and beaches. Last, but most important, the peril of catastrophic floods, which have ravaged the

Dutch land since time immemorial, will be ended forever.

The luckless inhabitants whom Pliny pitied were fisher-men, farmers, herdsmen, and artisans who by Roman times had already survived their inhospitable environment for some thousands of years. During this period, the soil, at least, steadily improved as the sea deposited rich clay against the dunes of what is now the northern province of Friesland. The *terps*, as these early Dutch called the mounds they strengthened or built, were as much as 40 acres in size, as high as 30 feet above ground level, to be safely out of reach of the sea.

Safely? Few things along the sea's edge are very safe, and every now and again an exceptionally high tide, a chance combination of wind and water and inland tempera-ture, swept over the terps, carrying off huts and fishing boats, drowning people and cattle. By the early Middle Ages, the long war between the Dutch and the sea had begun. The terps rose no higher; instead, dikes encircled all of Friesland. At first, the dikes were built to connect neighboring terps. When several of the mounds had been joined together by dikes, the combination was called a *polder*. Gradually, the polders in turn were joined by dikes. Almost at once an odd and disconcerting phenome-non developed: the more dikes that were built the harder the sea seemed to hit them.

It took a while before anybody realized that the tide is like any other force: the more it is confined, the more pres-sure it exerts. At the same time, the furious sea helped build the country, for against the earthen embankments it continually piled silt, providing more rich land that the embattled Dutch promptly claimed by building more dikes. The grassy barriers were improved, first by pegged-down mats of straw on their faces, then by stacked-up seaweed, then by timber piles and stone. To allow the rivers access to the sea and yet protect the low-lying land, even the inland river banks were lined with stout earthworks.

During the early dike-building era, Netherlanders continued to develop a sea-linked life. Fishing, always a national industry, improved radically. For reasons known only to the herring, this delicious and abundant fish quit its ancient spawning ground in the Baltic Sound during medieval times and began turning up in bigger and bigger numbers in the North Sea. The Dutch were soon catching so many herring they needed bigger boats to carry them, and presently they invented the broad-beamed *buss,* which enabled them to go farther, employ bigger nets, and salt the herring on board instead of having to race home before it spoiled. Soon they were peddling salted herring up and down the coast, especially in the Baltic but even all the way into the Mediterranean. This brought up the problem of return cargoes, and the Dutch fish peddlers became the freight haulers of western Europe. Their native polders did not afford timber to build ships, and it had to be imported from Scandinavia. Dutch commerce grew and grew, and Dutch ships traded and brawled all over the world, including its newly discovered distant portions. A flourishing Dutch kingdom arose with the aid of strenuous political and military efforts. Much of its territory lay below normal sea level.

Early in the seventeenth century the Amsterdam merchants who had grown wealthy in the trading observed that the lakes that characterized the northern part of the country would provide extremely profitable farmland if they could be drained. With the aid of the wheelbarrow and the wind-

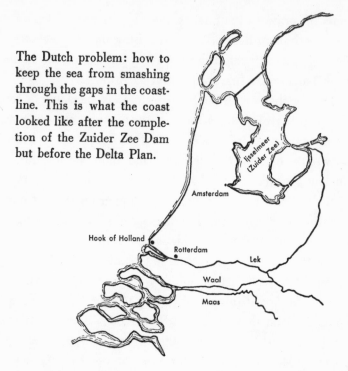

The Dutch problem: how to keep the sea from smashing through the gaps in the coastline. This is what the coast looked like after the completion of the Zuider Zee Dam but before the Delta Plan.

mill, invented during the course of the struggle against the sea, a series of remarkable Renaissance engineering projects expanded the Dutch homeland by many thousands of acres, the water-pumping windmill ultimately receiving assistance from eighteenth-century steam power.

In the nineteenth century, the biggest lake of all, the Haarlemmermeer, was drained. With the completion of this project, Dutch engineers turned their eyes on what at first glance seemed a fantastic project—draining the Zuider Zee. For years a brilliant engineer and cabinet minister, Dr. Cornelis Lely, pressed for approval of the bold scheme, but he only won it when in 1916 a severe storm from the northwest swept the Zuider over its banks and caused widespread havoc.

Unpredictable weather might any year bring catastrophe. The spring flood from the melting snows of Switzerland, meeting a high tide from the sea, created an annual peril; add a steady west wind and a severe storm and the Netherlands faced national disaster. Since the Middle Ages, the country had been visited by one hundred and twenty-five major floods. The worst, that of December 14, 1287, had drowned fifty thousand people. The Zuider Zee flood of 1916 was less destructive than that but serious enough to warrant Lely's barrier dam across the mouth of the Zuider.

The 20-mile-long work was the biggest engineering project of its day, costing 60 million hard, pre-World War II dollars and taking 9 years (1923–1932) to complete. It accomplished three important objectives:

1. It effectively barred the door against floods from the northwest.
2. It made possible the reclamation of some 550,000 acres of land by means of polders inside the new, fresh-water Lake Ijssel, now substituted for the Zuider Zee.
3. It shortened the coast line by 186 miles, cutting down erosion and so counteracting the soil subsidence and rising tides that had caused the country to "sink" inch by inch through the centuries.

The first point needs no elaboration, but perhaps the second and third do. The salinity problem is one that has intensified greatly in the twentieth-century Netherlands. Most crops are adversely affected by salt, or more precisely, by chloride in their water. Even the milk yield of cows declines sharply when the animals' drinking water has a high chloride content. Because of the long gradual sinking of the land area in relation to the sea level, the sea-water seepage under the dams and dikes is increasing. At the same time, in the Netherlands as everywhere the demand for fresh water constantly goes up. This results in a depletion of the fresh-water reservoir lying directly beneath the sand dunes all along the west coast from the Hook of Holland to Lake Ijssel. As this natural reservoir grows shallower, salty sea water seeps in under it to salinate the land.

The Zuider Zee project was not even completed before discussion began on the momentous Delta Plan, the decisive, if not the last, battle of the war. The depressed years of the 1930's were not favorable to so vast an undertaking, and before anything could be done, the war intervened with multiple catastrophes, the last two being the bomb-flooding of Walcheren Island by the Allies and the demolition-flooding of Wieringermeer Polder by the Germans. Repairing the damage at Walcheren was a herculean task that brought about a revolution in dike engineering. For the first time, the caisson, that indispensable tool of bridge builders, was employed. The Dutch used concrete caissons, weighing up to 3,800 tons, built in Britain for use in artificial invasion harbors. The giant boxes were divided into compartments by interior bulkheads, and could be floated into position and sunk by opening valves.

The success of the Walcheren operation greatly encouraged Dutch engineers to consider the Delta Plan. In comparison with the Zuider Zee scheme, this was hugely complicated. The Zuider Zee work had consisted essentially of a single massive wall with sluice gates to permit gradual expulsion of sea water by fresh water from the rivers. The

Delta Plan involved a whole series of closures, not all of them obvious.

The southernmost estuary, the Wester Scheldt, is the arm that reaches the port of Antwerp. In their roistering heyday of the sixteenth century, when the Dutch were throwing their weight around freely, they shut off traffic on the Wester Scheldt and so ruined their Belgian rival. It took an invading French Revolutionary army to reopen the estuary, but the Dutch have never tried closing it since, and they aren't about to. Therefore, the Delta planners had to figure on leaving the Wester Scheldt unblocked.

The Netherlands' own chief port, Rotterdam, like Antwerp, is situated as high up as deep-draft vessels can go. That arm too, the New Waterway, must be kept open, and right here is the real stickler of the whole puzzle. Leaving the Wester Scheldt open for Antwerp does not affect the rest of the Delta, except that it keeps one stretch of Dutch shore line saline, but the Rotterdam problem is something else again.

The two largest rivers, the Maas (Meuse) and the Rhine, approach the Netherlands on a parallel course, flowing north in tandem, then turning west—the Rhine wheeling above the Maas—plunging on toward the sea, yet staying in their separate beds till they reach the edge of the ocean, when they rush together at last to meet the powerful inflowing tide. The result of this clash of two rivers and the sea—with the Scheldt to the south—is the creation of an archipelago of sandy, storm-beaten islands and peninsulas separated by straits of shallow, racing, back-and-forth, sea-and-river water that almost ruins the whole region for any useful human purpose. On the isles and peninsulas, the polders resist the waters like forts, but like forts, they defend only what lies within their own walls.

To transform the region into a storm-secure, maximum-yield agricultural-industrial enclave, at the same time to keep the port of Rotterdam open and yet to desalt the hinterland of Rotterdam—that is the problem. The map shows where the dams must be built. The major ones, built to hold back the ocean, are obvious—across the mouths of the Veersche Gat, the Ooster Scheldt, the Grevelingen, and the Haringvliet. The Brielsche Maas, the small estuary just south of the New Waterway, was closed by a dam in 1950. But what was to prevent the ocean tide from pouring up the New Waterway and salting all the Rotterdam hinterland, as it had done for centuries?

The solution is one of the neatest engineering tricks of the century. Nearly the whole volume of current from the Rhine and Maas is shepherded into the single narrow channel of the New Waterway, where its force is enough to

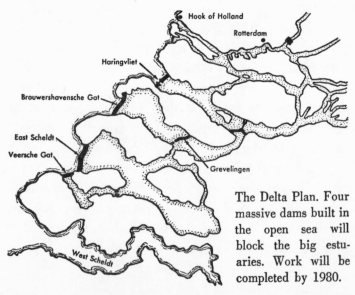

The Delta Plan. Four massive dams built in the open sea will block the big estuaries. Work will be completed by 1980.

wrestle the mighty tidal surge and force it back oceanward.

To accomplish this is part of the mission of the four secondary dams. These will divide the delta into two regions—a giant, tideless, fresh-water reservoir in the south, and the cleverly controlled fresh-water current in the north. The other half of their mission will be to help in the construction of the main dams.

The whole scheme goes like this:

1. The *Wester Scheldt* to be left open, but its banks to be protected by new, higher dikes.

2. The *Veersche Gat*, entrance to the Zandcreek, to be blocked by a dam. To prevent tides from coming around Noord Beveland and playing havoc with construction, a secondary dam to be built at the eastern end of the Zandcreek.

3. The *Ooster Scheldt* to be blocked by a stupendous dam some 5 miles long.

4. The *Brouwershavensche Gat* to be blocked by a dam nearly as long. As a necessary preliminary, a secondary dam to be built at the eastern end of the Grevelingen, just north of the town of Bruinisse, where the flood tides from either side of the island of Schouwen-Duiveland meet.

5. The *Volkerak* to be closed by a secondary dam, completing the isolation of the southern region. Like the other secondary dams, this one is vital to a control of tides during construction of the major sea barriers, but it also has an important permanent function: equipped with lock and sluice gates, it will control the water level in the whole southern basin.

The Rhine and the Maas, as we have observed, discharge into the region north of the Volkerak. When they are in flood in winter or early spring, the Volkerak Dam will be

opened to permit flow into the southern basin, building up
the water level to maximum for agricultural demands during the summer. A subtlety of the scheme is the allowance
for discharge of some water into the ocean from time to
time, via the two canals that cross Walcheren and Zuid
Beveland to get rid of the silt that will accumulate in the
absence of tidal flow.

6. The *Haringvliet* to be blocked by a primary dam 3
miles long, equipped with giant sluice gates. These will
permit a large degree of control over the water level in the
northern basin and let the masses of ice from the upper
Rhine and Maas escape.

7. The *Storm Barrier*, a secondary dam at the mouth of
the Hollandsche Ijssel River, to close this quiet river off in
case of exceptionally high flood tides and so protect the
very low land along its shores.

8. Higher embankments all along the New Waterway
and the Lek, to protect against the higher water level. The
whole large island of Ijsselmonde, south of Rotterdam, to
be so protected.

By the early 1950's the Delta Plan had been worked out
in minute detail. Dr. Johan Van Veen, head of the engineering group working on the project, urged the government to put the scheme into effect as soon as possible. He
warned that there was a possibility, though admittedly re-
mote, of a severe storm flood breaking through existing sea
defenses. On January 29, 1953, Van Veen submitted proposals embodying his engineers' most up-to-date blue-
prints. That was a Thursday. On Saturday the nation hung
out flags to celebrate the birthday of Crown Princess Bea-
trix, and by the end of the day a number of patriotic citi-
zens found that their flags were in tatters. The high wind

was one of the four disaster factors that were once more to fall into fatal random coincidence. The mountain snows of Switzerland were melting, sending the spring torrents into the Rhine, Maas and Scheldt rivers. The wind, steadily from the northwest, now was blowing a gale. And at night came the high tide. The water roiled over the dikes throughout the delta, turning to attack the sea defenses from the land side. The wind refused to let up. It still blew a storm at next high tide, and the water now smashed through the weakened dikes, creating *flow gaps*. Through such gaps the water moved freely back and forth, rapidly wearing away the exposed corners and widening the gateway. When this stage is reached, there is nothing to be done—the battle is lost. Three hundred miles of dikes were smashed, 375,000 acres of soil inundated, 1,835 persons perished, and 47,300 houses, farms, and schools were destroyed or damaged. The direct cost in money was more than half a billion dollars.

As in the case of the Zuider Zee, disaster spurred action. The Delta Committee was set up on February 21, and the Delta Plan, modified in the light of the experience gained in the flood, was begun. The target dates were:

> 1961: the Veersche Gat
> 1968: the Haringvliet
> 1970: the Brouwershavensche Gat
> 1978: the Ooster Scheldt

The secondary dams, whose main function was to facilitate construction of the major barriers, were started first. The Storm Barrier across the Hollandsche Ijssel was built at once for immediate protection of the low lands northeast of Rotterdam. A steel door 85 yards wide and nearly 12

yards high was equipped with counterweights so that it
could be raised and lowered like a lift bridge or a sluice
gate. Locks permitted shipping to pass.

The first major dam undertaken was the Veersche Gat,
southernmost and smallest of the four sea barriers. Though
the smallest, it was by no means small—the channel is
about a thousand yards wide—and its construction presented the same great basic problem that the bigger dams
to the north did—closure. To block off a tidal estuary,
dams are built out from either shore to the middle. The
work near the shore is easy, even if the water is deep, but
as the channel is narrowed, the tidal race becomes swifter,
as the same volume of water tries to squeeze through a
smaller opening in the same time. In 1932, the Zuider Zee
closure had been a hazardous proposition; even though the
water was relatively shallow and still, dams made the depth
at final closure only 12 feet. But important advances had

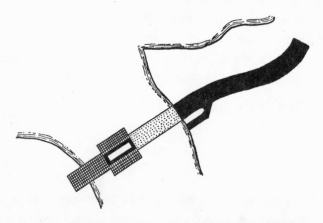

The Veersche Gat holds back the sea. The broad sandbank on the
right (black) was first closed with a dike. The channel bed was
prepared with sill work (cross hatching). The dike was then built
out into the midchannel (dotted section). Finally, the central gap
was sealed with caissons (white rectangle).

been made—above all, the invaluable caisson. The Dutch had made several improvements in the caisson, such as creation of prefabricated sections that could be assembled into various sizes. For the Veersche Gat dam, they built caissons equipped with vertical sliding gates. To tow the box into position in the channel, they lowered (closed) the gate. Once it was sunk, they raised the gate, so the tide could flow through freely. Extensive preparation of the sea bed was carried out first, with a *sill* constructed by dredging a trench and sinking flexible mattresses of nylon mesh, laid by a machine that rolled along the sea bottom. The mattresses give the caissons a firm footing, so that currents do not swirl under and damage them.

Meanwhile, an embankment was built out from the western shore to the point where the caissons were to take over. Then one by one the seven giant caissons were towed out, positioned, and sunk. With the caissons open to permit the tide to flow through, the eastern embankment was constructed. Then came the final step—simultaneous closure of the seven caisson gates—and the Veersche Gat was shut to the sea.

The secondary dam at the eastern end of the Zandcreek having already been completed, one considerable body of water was now isolated and tideless.

By the time the Veersche Gat dam was completed in 1961, work on the Haringvliet, next in order of size of the four primary barriers, was already well under way. The Haringvliet structure, it will be recalled, was planned with sluice gates to control the water level of the northern basin and to permit outflow of Rhine-Maas ice and water during the spring flood. The Haringvliet is about 3½ miles wide, and the selection of the site for the barrier was made only after exhaustive studies and long debate.

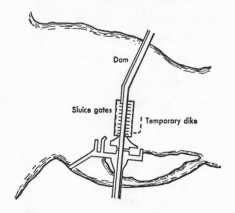

Blocking the sea: The Haringvliet Dam requires 17 sluice gates to allow the icy spring torrents to pass. A shipping lock is provided in the southwest corner.

There were three possibilities. The outermost would do the best job of shortening the coast line, a major objective of the whole plan, but it was finally rejected because the exposed location made it too costly and hazardous to undertake. The innermost, near Hellevoetsluis, would provide the most sheltered construction site, but it was calculated that such a location would threaten the coast lines of the estuary with erosion. The middle site, linking the western end of the isle of Plaat van Scheelhoek with the Voorne shore opposite, was chosen.

The next question was the location of the sluice structure, whose seventeen gates, each 62 yards wide, separated by 6-yard-wide piers, would form almost a quarter of the entire dam. The configuration of the sea bottom determined the choice. The deep channel lay close to the Voorne shore; therefore the sluice structure was situated in midchannel, to be connected by a long embankment to Voorne and by a short one to Scheelhoek.

A structure at once as delicate and as massive as the Haringvliet sluice gates could hardly be built in an open tidal race. The first step was to create an island and install the sluice gates on the island. This required a cofferdam of unheard-of proportions. Since the entire length of the sluice-gate structure was 1,092 yards, the cofferdam, or ring dike, was designed as a rectangle with rounded corners, 1,500 yards in length; it is 600 yards wide, with a hook added on the sheltered side to provide a harbor for construction vessels. Dumping of clay began on February 15, 1957; at first, it was used to form a bank in the direction of the stream. Clay was dredged from the Hollandsch Diep a few miles inshore, and sand, from the adjacent sea bed. The lower slopes of the bank were protected by *fascine mattresses* made of bundles of willows sunk in place by stones. Especially heavy stone—basalt—was imported from Germany for the purpose. The exact sequence in which various parts of the huge island ring were built up was determined in advance by testing models, which showed how the successive stages of construction would deflect the tidal currents.

While the cofferdam work was going on, the embankment connecting the future sluice-gate structure with the Voorne shore was built; it was closed in the middle by twenty caissons towed out in units of three and four. This work was finished by the end of summer, though it was given one setback by a gale that blew up in August. Also by the end of summer, the cofferdam wall, or dike, on the seaward side was complete, and a good start made on the sheltered side. Work was pushed through the winter and the ring built up of sand, asphalt, and sheet piling—the completed sluice substructure containing twenty-two thousand concrete piles, with 28,800 tons of steel. It is hardly necessary to mention that this is the biggest cofferdam ever built.

Behind its protection, the construction of the massive sluice gates was begun; it will be complete in 1968. Hydraulic machinery installed in each pier will operate the gates. Enormous prestressed-concrete beams 40 feet deep will span the gate openings, and over the top a 70-foot-wide automobile highway will run. This highway will also ride over the top of the Brouwershavensche Gat, Ooster Scheldt, and Veersche Gat dams, joining the present highway, which connects Walcheren with Bergen op Zoom and the interior. The secondary dam over the Volkerak will also have a section of highway on top—the projected new main highway from Rotterdam to Antwerp, which will cross the Hollandsch Diep by a bridge that will join the dam at right angles. This is another unique piece of engineering—a bridge, a dam, and a highway all combined in one structure.

Dutch engineers, long pre-eminent in hydraulic and sea-defense works, have learned much in the first 10 years of the Delta Plan, which appears certain to be completed by the target date of 1980. They have also profited from the experience of other countries, just as the Dutch experience will in turn be valuable in other parts of the world. For example, the big secondary dam over the Grevelingen, the essential preliminary to the Brouwershavensche Gat barrier, made use of a very novel and successful technique of closure. Instead of sinking caissons as in the Veersche Gat closure, the Dutch, in collaboration with a French contractor, strung a mile-long cableway over the water and ran suspended dump cars across it. The tower at one end of the monorail had a turntable to send the cars back. Each Diesel-powered car was manned by a driver who ran it across at 11 mph, dumping 11 tons of rock fill at the designated spot.

Nowhere on the face of the earth has a more visible transformation been wrought by man's own hand.

9
The Biggest Road:
The Interstate Highway System

". . . *the sixlane highway*
that arched the reedy rivers and skirted the fields
of red clover,
now in whine of windfriction, hiss of tires, valve-
chatter, grumble of diesels, drone of exhausts,
plunges under a rampaging bridge,
sixlane under sixlane"

JOHN DOS PASSOS, *U.S.A. Revisited*

SIXTY YEARS AGO, most American families lived lives of perpetual isolation, on farms and in small towns, able to travel only a few miles by buggy or spring wagon unless a major catastrophe, such as a foreclosure, drove them to the hardship of a long journey. In *A Son of the Middle Border*, Hamlin Garland tells how he and his brother made a trip east to see Boston. Traveling around Massachusetts on foot, stopping to work for their board at farms, they found families that had never been farther from home than the nearest town, to whom the visitors from the Midwest appeared as a couple of Marco Polos back from Cathay.

This isolation had strangling consequences—cultural, economic, and political. It has been ended by several technological developments—radio, TV, airplanes. Far and away the most important has been the automobile, without which twentieth-century America is hard to imagine. The automobile itself has remained essentially unchanged for about fifty years. What has changed is the road. The culmination of its development is the network of hard, rigid, all-weather surfaces on which people can drive from New York to Chicago in two days without hitting a traffic light; by-pass Boston or Buffalo, once worth an hour's irritation on a hot summer day; drive downtown in Detroit at a steady 65 mph to within two blocks of their destination. Vacation trips are longer and cheaper, national parks and forests are within week-end reach of city dwellers, neighbors who have moved to opposite sides of a city can easily get together again. Employees can drive twice as far to work in half the time, which creates new economies in plant locations. Truck-haul time and costs are cut, helping farmers and businesses reach markets faster and cheaper and saving consumers money.

People who prefer the old-fashioned highways that wind through the small towns, giving a better view of the countryside, owe a debt to the Interstate Highway System too, for it has made possible the preservation of the old routes in all their charm. By siphoning off most of the traffic, the 41,000-mile Interstate Highway has given a new lease to hundreds of highways otherwise doomed to glut and ruin.

There is something in all of us that enjoys criticizing the present in terms of an allegedly better past. Since its beginnings, the automobile age has inspired nostalgic sentiment for the unpleasant, uncomfortable, stultifying, and happily brief horse-and-buggy age. The automobile will probably have to vanish before its charms are sung, but unlike the horse and buggy, the automobile is a long way from vanishing. Earth-surface traffic in the year 2000 will be from six to twenty times as heavy as it is now, and while a lot of that will be by monorail, automatic devices, conventional rail, and so on, the core of the transport system, then as now, will be the road. Automobiles, trucks, and buses may not be gasoline-powered, and they will be highly automated, but they will run on roads just as today's cars do.

In America, the road-building business got started by General Braddock and George Washington. Washington reconnoitered a trail from the headwaters of the Potomac to those of the Monongahela and felled trees to a breadth of 6 feet. Braddock followed the next year and widened the road to 12 feet. This enabled him to march his whole army with wagons and artillery deep into the wilderness, which turned out to be not too good an idea. But a generation later settlers began using General Braddock's road to cross the mountains into the Ohio country, and in 1811, it was chosen as the basis for America's first federally aided highway program, the justly celebrated National Pike, which ran from Cumberland, Maryland, through Uniontown, Pennsylvania, to Wheeling on the Ohio, paved with a macadam surface of several layers of crushed rock. Drainage was provided by a system of spillways and culverts, and across the streams beautiful stone-arch bridges were built. Traffic on the National Pike permanently fixed the new American custom of driving on the right. Originally, wagoners on this continent had followed the British practice of driving on the left, but the introduction of the Conestoga wagon, whose oxen had to be guided from the left side of the seat, changed that.

The National Pike raised a significant furor on constitutional grounds. President Monroe vetoed a bill to raise funds by tollgates operated by the federal government, but the road was so popular with Monroe's Jeffersonian-Democrat supporters in the West, that two years later he decided federal support of it was constitutional after all and approved an appropriation for its repair. Once the road was put in shape it was turned over to the states it passed through. This established a crucial precedent for financing and maintaining United States highways. What it amounts to is that the federal government pays a varying but substantial share of the highways' costs and the states own them.

The National Pike was followed by a considerable hiatus in federal road building. First the canals and then the railroads took the center of the transportation stage, far surpassing as they did horse- and ox-drawn wagons in carrying power. Roads were for local traffic only, for farmers to move their grain to the elevator and take their families to church. Anything that moved long distances went by rail or water. By 1890, there were 2 million miles of roads in the United States, almost all of them dirt.

Sinclair Lewis memorialized the isolation of the small town in *Main Street*, but re-examined today, Lewis's fictional art suffers from myopia. The social condition Lewis deplored was vanishing forever at the very time that he was writing about it, and Lewis apparently never noticed what was going on. *Main Street* appeared in 1920, having occupied its author's mind the better part of the two previous decades, according to his own account. Yet it was these two decades that witnessed the revolution wrought by the gasoline engine and pneumatic tire.

The automobile did not merely break through the isolation of rural America in a hundred ways; it hastened the urbanization process. Instead of a vast warren of tiny communities all much alike but all separated from each other, the United States was turning into a complex of metropolitan centers in close intercommunication. Though many elements contributed to this transformation, the automobile was certainly one of the most important.

By 1910, most states were in the road business in a sizable way, and by 1920, when *Main Street* appeared, a dramatic shift had taken place. Instead of 2 million miles of dirt roads, there were now 3 million, but, in addition, there were 300,000 miles of "improved roads," and these were carrying far more than their ratio of traffic. Not all of these "improved" roads were hard-surfaced—every middle-aged motorist of today remembers the gravel roads that abounded in the 1920's. They were dusty, but serviceable —automobiles could travel them at speeds undreamed of by drivers a couple of decades earlier. In fact, simple gravel was found better for automobile traffic than macadam, which tended to come apart under the weight of the new vehicles. Tars, asphalts, and Portland-cement concrete were substituted as binders, and a few years later the hot bituminous mixture that remains the basis of hard-surface roads today was developed. In 1904, there were only 18 miles of bituminous-paved rural roads (in Massachusetts and Ohio), but by 1914, 10,500 miles had been laid. By that time, the gasoline engine had introduced a fresh demand on surfaces—trucks. They required a more rigid pavement, which was produced by various combinations of bituminous concrete, brick, and Portland-cement concrete on a concrete base. Research and experience steadily improved low-cost hard-surfacing.

But the demand of the multiplying army of gas buggies for more roads, better roads, more and more better and better roads was virtually insatiable. By a stroke of good luck, the fuel the autos ran on proved highly susceptible to the excise tax. State highway departments were set up that were essentially engineering boards with a bit of politics thrown in, whose function was to take 25 or 30 cents from the motorist every time he bought gas and then use the money to build him new roads. The oil companies had no objection since more roads meant more auto travel and more gas consumption.

With astonishing rapidity, the dirt roads were transformed into hard surfaces. The 3 million miles of dirt and 300,000 miles of surfaced roads of 1920 changed only very slightly in total volume, but by midcentury the ratio was reversed. Four types of road, nearly all paved, comprised America's network. In descending order of mileage, they are:

1. Local roads and streets, carrying little through traffic.
2. Collectors and distributors, linking the locals with the bigger arteries.
3. Major conventional highways.
4. Freeways and expressways.

Freeways and expressways are characterized by more access control and grade separations at intersections. Expressways generally have only partial access control, freeways total control.

Responsibility for building, maintaining, and operating the first three classes of road rests with state and local authorities, even though federal funds have been contributed on one basis or another to more than 800,000 miles of them. The federal government's highway arm is the Bureau of Public Roads of the Department of Commerce. The bureau was founded in 1893, at the very outset of the automobile age, principally in response to the demands of the swarm of bicyclists who had just appeared on the scene. It first was involved with federal aid in 1916, but the program remained fairly modest through the 1920's and even the 1930's. Long-distance highways in the United States remained essentially link-ups of state roads, though some were built with preplanned cooperation of two or more states. However, by the late 1930's it was beginning to be apparent that the country needed a new type of long-distance highway, one that would provide extremely long stretches of safe, high-speed travel. The atmosphere of the New Deal 1930's was congenial to the grandiose idea of a giant nationwide express-highway system. The method that had been developed earlier on federal-aid highways had proved practical and satisfactory to all parties. Essentially, the state highway department picks the projects, hires the contractors and engineers, then turns to the federal government for reimbursement of the major share of the cost. The federal government, through the Bureau of Public Roads, examines and approves each project before contracts are signed. The bureau also contributes research and advice.

Though federal aid initially came from general tax funds, the real source of highway-construction costs was tardily identified in the Highway Trust Fund Act of 1956, which earmarked federal gasoline taxes and other highway-related revenue for highway expenditures. Finally, there was one more factor favoring the idea of a national expressway system in 1939: the international situation. As it turned out, that situation deteriorated too rapidly, in the euphemism of diplomats, for highway construction to be undertaken in its name, but the war gave Congress a strong push toward security-mindedness, and in 1944, following various studies, it directed that the National System of Interstate and Defense Highways, commonly known as the Interstate Highway System, be established. Planning was carried forward immediately, though construction did not start until the mid-1950's.

The program that won the approval of Congress consisted of 41,000 miles of highway construction. This is a very modest bit of road building, taken strictly in the linear sense. It represents only one ninetieth of the United States road, street, and highway total. Virtually every country of any size has many more roads than that, and practically any civilized country has more paved roads. Yet the Interstate Highway System is by far the most ambitious highway construction program ever undertaken by any country anywhere. Hitler's much-trumpeted *autobahn* network was a trifle by comparison. Its cost works out to a bit over $1 billion per 1,000 miles, or $47 billion for the whole job, which will be completed in 1972. The system will link together 90 percent of all United States cities of 50,000 or more. It will bind well over half of the urban population together, including almost half of the rural population along its right of way. It will carry 20 percent of all United States automobile traffic. Streams of workers were pouring over the Interstate Highway System to and from their jobs long before the network's completion, while raw materials, semifinished manufactures, and finished products crisscrossed America on it.

Following the custom established years ago by the Bureau of Roads and the state highway departments, the interstate routes are given even numbers for east-west routes, odd for north-south ones. But to avoid confusion with the old United States routes, the low-numbered routes are in the west and south. The main interstate routes across the country from Atlantic to Pacific are:

Interstate 90. As the Massachusetts Turnpike, it crosses the Berkshires, joins the New York Thruway to Albany, Rochester, and Buffalo, and turns southwest to skirt Lake Erie as the Ohio Turnpike. At Cleveland, it joins Interstate 80, and as that route it rolls across western Ohio, Indiana, and Illinois to Chicago. Once more dividing into its components, as Interstate 90 it runs north through Wisconsin, then across southern Minnesota, South Dakota (through the Black Hills, close to Mount Rushmore), a corner of Wyoming, southwest Montana (passing Billings, Butte, and Missoula), up across the Idaho panhandle (Coeur d'Alene), and across Washington by way of Spokane and Ellensburg, entering Seattle by way of the world's biggest pontoon bridge, over Lake Washington.

Interstate 80. From Philadelphia it starts out as the many-tunneled Pennsylvania Turnpike, the rather amazing residue of a long-forgotten railroad-rate feud of two robber barons, John D. Rockefeller and Commodore Cornelius Vanderbilt, during which Rockefeller went so far as to build a roadbed for a railroad of his own. The Rockefeller railroad was never built, but forty years later a group of promoters built a toll road on it, now absorbed into a major transcontinental route. Interstate 80 continues through Ohio and Indiana to Chicago; then, parting from its temporary companion, Interstate 90, heads west via

Rock Island, site of the Mississippi's first bridge, through the waving corn fields of Iowa, the envy of Khrushchev, over the Missouri at Omaha, across Nebraska, southern Wyoming (passing Cheyenne, Laramie, and Fort Bridger, souvenirs of the old West), to Echo Junction, in the northeast corner of Utah. Here it divides. As Interstate 80 North, it traverses southern Idaho and northern Oregon to Portland, the modern version of one of America's great historic routes, known to the buffalo and the Indian hunter —the legendary Oregon Trail.

Interstate 80 South (labeled just 80 on the route signs) skirts Salt Lake City, where the sea gulls saved the Mormons from the grasshoppers, crosses mountain and desert haunted by ghosts of the Donner party, sweeps south to Reno, and enters the fabled Sierra Nevada range. It winds through these forbidding snow-covered peaks, over Donner Pass to Sacramento, and ultimately Oakland and San Francisco, via the great cantilever-suspension-viaduct-rock-tunnel complex of the Bay Bridge.

Interstate 70. This is a foreshortened transcontinental route, running from Pennsylvania through Columbus and Indianapolis to the Mississippi at St. Louis, then west, through Kansas City and Topeka to Denver. Seventy miles west of Denver it passes through the first tunnel ever driven through the Continental Divide, a 9,000-foot bore at Straight Creek, Colorado. Interstate 70 terminates at Cove Fort, Utah, where it junctions with Interstate 15 running north and south.

Interstate 40. This is the Southern Pacific Freeway. Kicking off at Greensboro, in the middle of North Carolina, it winds up and over the Great Smokies to Knoxville, runs via Nashville to Memphis and across the big river through Little Rock and, following in the footsteps of the land rush of 1889, over the plains of Oklahoma, then through the Texas panhandle to New Mexico by way of Albuquerque and Flagstaff, over desert and mountains (including the ghost town of Calico) to Los Angeles.

Interstate 10 and *20*. The far southern route is a gigantic fork, starting from South Carolina (20) and from Jacksonville, Florida (10), the pincers meeting west of the Pecos, where Judge Bean was once the law, passing on as Interstate 10 along the Rio Grande to El Paso, through southern New Mexico (running by both Carlsbad Caverns and White Sands Proving Ground), to Los Angeles, with little Interstate 8 taking off south of Phoenix and running to San Diego.

These even-numbered transcontinental expressway routes are crisscrossed by a more intricate series of odd-numbered routes running north and south.

Interstate 95 is the longest, and easternmost, of the north-south routes. Picking up from the Canadian border at Houlton, Maine, it roams through wooded northern New England countryside, then stilt-walks thickly industrial southern-coastal New England (including Boston and Providence), runs along Long Island Sound as the Connecticut Turnpike (or New England Thruway), over the George Washington Bridge to New Jersey, on to Philadelphia, Baltimore, and Washington, D.C., over the Potomac, past the Civil War battlefields to Richmond, through southern Virginia and the Carolinas, then, hugging the coast, to Savannah, where it meets Interstate 16, which from Atlanta follows in the tracks of Sherman's dashing Yankee boys. On down the long coast, Interstate 95 passes Jacksonville and Daytona Beach, where the racing cars set records, on the way to Miami.

Interstate 89, 91, 81, 79. These also all begin at the Canadian borders of New England and New York, but none go all the way south. Instead, they make connections that lead the rest of the way to the Gulf of Mexico with Interstate 81, 85, and others. Interstate 77 from Cleveland joins 85 at Charlotte, 65 at Montgomery, and runs on to Mobile.

Interstate 65 runs south from Chicago by way of Indianapolis, a mighty interstate hub, through Louisville, Nashville, and Birmingham to Mobile. En route it picks up Interstate 71 from Cleveland and Cincinnati, 69 from Michigan, and 59 from Chattanooga.

Interstate 55 and *57* also run south from Chicago; 55 crosses the Mississippi at St. Louis and, descending the right bank, junctions with 57 at Sikeston, Missouri, recrossing the river at Memphis and flowing through the state of Mississippi into Louisiana to join Interstate 10 above New Orleans.

Interstate 35 begins at Duluth, the iron port, running almost due south for Minneapolis, St. Paul, and Des Moines, bending a little to the west from St. Joseph, Missouri, to meet Interstate 29, coming south from Grand Forks, North Dakota, at Kansas City, another major interstate hub. From there, 35 turns sharply southwest to Wichita, then drops straight south again to Oklahoma City, Fort Worth, Austin, and San Antonio, curving west to terminate in the streets of Laredo.

Interstate 25, far to the west in the most sparsely populated, but most rapidly growing, belt of America, is launched from Buffalo, Wyoming (where 90 takes you northwest to Billings, Montana); it runs down through Casper and Cheyenne to Denver, Pueblo, Santa Fe, and Albuquerque, rolling effortlessly through country Kit Carson explored foot by rugged foot and on to meet Interstate 10 near the border at Las Cruces, New Mexico.

Interstate 15, really out in the wide-open spaces, comes down from the Canadian border just north of Sweetgrass, Montana, through cowboy country—Great Falls, Helena, and Butte, runs on through Idaho east of the panhandle, passes Ogden, Utah, and Salt Lake City, and then curves southwest through Las Vegas (Death Valley lies to the west) to Los Angeles.

Interstate 5 is the westernmost of the great north-south routes. From the border on the coast of Puget Sound, it passes Seattle, Portland, Salem, and Grant's Pass and runs through the California mountains via Central Valley to Sacramento, where it connects with a net of short interstate routes to the Bay area and then moves south through green valleys and desert to Los Angeles and San Diego where, in the deep southwest corner of the country, it meets Interstate 8.

How does one go about laying 41,000 miles of expressway? Despite dislocations, right-of-way problems, and squabbles sometimes exploding into headlines, the interstate construction has been, for history's biggest public-works program, rather inconspicuous. Nearly everyone, though, is pretty well aware of the fact that mechanized monsters play the main role in today's sophisticated road building. Unskilled labor is still used, but the thoroughly trained operator of a big machine is the real road builder. The best known of the machines is, of course, the bulldozer, which is the trailblazer—digging, scalping, carving the landscape, leveling whatever lies in the road's path. This includes man-made structures, though it is not true that the bulldozer, as some critics imply, has a special affinity for knocking down churches, historic landmarks, and fine old houses.

In planning the road the engineers locate the route so that material cut from hills is about equal to that required for embankments across valleys and then adjust this so the "grade" or slope is not too steep for trucks. Building a road suitable for high speed and trucking is invariably a major earth-moving job. An average mile of rural highway on the Interstate Highway System demands ½ million cubic yards of excavation. Most of this earth moving is done by the *hauling scraper,* a combination of power shovel and earth hauler. The scraper pushes into the earth, loads itself at 1 cubic yard a second, and moves to the dump area at 25 mph. If the haul is long, heavy off-highway hauling units even larger than the giant hauling scrapers are used. If it is rocky, jumbo drills, such as those used in tunneling, may be called in to drill holes for blasting. The ease with which the army of crawling, hauling, digging, gouging, dirt-moving machines refashion the terrain, removing the side of a hill, filling in a ravine, or cutting through a ridge permits total elimination of steep grades and sharp curves.

Once the bulldozer and scraper are finished, massive rollers and tampers wheel in on tremendous high-pressure tires to compact the earth. Ultimately, all the loading of future traffic will be pressing down on this subgrade, so it must be hard, firm, and uniform. Contractors who have large amounts of expensive equipment tied up are in a hurry, and yet this compacting job must be done exactly right. Modern science has come to the rescue in this case: isotope gauges permit engineers to test compaction quickly and with extreme accuracy.

A base course of gravel or crushed stone is laid on the compacted embankment. Once a dump-truck job, this is now a chore for a big combination spreader, which lays the gravel with nice uniformity. New electronic devices make it possible to spread successive courses to a fine tolerance in minimum time. The gravel is produced in minimum time, too, thanks to new "portable" rock crushers. Bituminous concrete-mixing plants have also advanced steadily in portability and quality control.

The number and thickness of layers that go into a section of interstate highway depend on the kind of soil underneath. On a typical section of an older part of the system, up to 18 inches of rough stone went into the first layer, the subgrade. After it was compacted, a 6-inch layer of gravel was spread, the *subbase*. Next comes 7 inches of *macadam*, gravel stuck together with a binder, which is the *base*. Finally come 4½ inches of asphaltic concrete.

This produces a *flexible*, or *bituminous*, pavement, but more and more engineers are favoring rigid pavements of Portland-cement concrete, 8 to 10 inches thick, laid directly on top of a single granular layer several inches thick, which has been laid on the subgrade. The advantage of the more rigid pavement is that it spreads the loading of a passing truck over a wider area of the subgrade.

Technologically, the Interstate Highway System does not represent major departures in road building but rather an impressive advance deriving from a great number of minor improvements. Most of these minor improvements are directly attributable to the continuous research program, which is an integral part of the Interstate program.

Studies carried out by the Bureau of Roads (or by universities operating on grants) cover every phase of road building, from soils and foundations to condemnation proceedings. What can be added to concrete mixtures to enable them to better resist the scaling effect of de-icing agents? How will a bridge deck made of lightweight aggregate concrete stand up? What kind of paint will inhibit rust best on bridge-truss members? Can radioisotopes be effectively used to measure paint durability? What is the best way to evaluate the hardening characteristics of asphalt? How can sand drain be stabilized under a highway foundation? (Sometimes you cannot route a road around a swamp, you have to carry it right through.) What are the economic effects of the accessibility of an expressway on adjacent land use? What is the effect of increasing the ratio of small cars to the traffic stream? (There isn't any.) These are among the literally thousands of questions that the Interstate Highway System is helping answer. The answers will be valuable not only to the federal and state governments in future projects, but to foreign countries too. The Pan-American Highway is, of course, an important link carrying the Interstate Highway System to Alaska and through Central America, but beyond this road, outside of North America many roads in underdeveloped countries are built with the aid of knowledge gathered by the experience and research of the Bureau of Roads.

To return to the actual construction of interstate highways, about four fifths of the system is constructed on new locations. Of the remaining fifth, some mileage consists of freeways or expressways built before 1956 and some is a matter of doubling an existing road by building a separate roadway alongside it to make a divided highway. Over 2,000 miles are state-built toll roads, and thereby hangs a hot controversy. The American Automobile Association says, with considerable justice, that the New York Thruway, the Pennsylvania Turnpike, the New Jersey Turnpike, and others represent a "conspiracy of stupidity," which forces motorists to pay twice for the same road. In fact, the motorist pays three times for the road, because the 4 percent (or more), 25-year (or more), tax-free bonds for such roads add up in interest and principal to at least double the contracted price. Besides all that, the motorist even has to pay for the toll booths and collectors.

On the other hand, the 90 percent of the Interstate Highway System construction costs that the federal government assumes comes directly out of the pocket of the motorist in gas and other automobile taxes. Congress has laid down a rule that no federal funds can go toward helping to build a toll road. But in many cases—the Baltimore-Delaware Expressway, for example—investors are willing to bet that motorists will use their road—and they do.

Interstate design standards incorporate the latest proven features to provide "safe and tension-free driving." Sweeping curves and easy grades make vehicle-handling and visibility optimum (speed regulation is state controlled). Where they are needed to provide for local traffic, frontage roads running alongside the freeway are provided, eliminating the need for access to the big road.

Each traffic lane is at least 12 feet wide, with medians of at least 36 feet, except in certain mountainous and urban locations that do not permit so generous a breadth. An especially distinguished design feature of Interstate highways is the complete separation of opposing roadways in many places where they can conveniently be placed on opposite sides of a stream or at two different levels of a hillside. This generally costs no more and often is actually cheaper. Apart from its agreeable aesthetic quality, the separation provides another safety feature by reducing driver monotony.

Sometimes, the intense space-saving demands of urban sections may produce a scenic surprise. Interstate 24 had to get somehow through Chattanooga, a city jammed between the Moccasin Bend of the Tennessee River and Lookout Mountain. The engineers hit on the only possible economical route—right in the river. The stretch of Interstate 24 passing through Chattanooga runs on an embankment built up on the left bank of the Tennessee, and at two points runs over bridges (multiple-span, prestressed-concrete, box girder) built parallel to instead of across a major river.

Speaking of highway aesthetics, in 1958 Congress adopted a policy of control of outdoor advertising. In those sections of the Interstate Highway System outside commercial and industrial zones, a state that agrees to exercise control of billboards gets an extra ½ percent of the construction cost as a bonus. In 1965, further anti-billboard and anti-junkyard provisions were enacted.

Exactly how big is the Interstate Highway System? Its 41,000 miles, mostly of four-lane roads, add up to 170,000 lane-miles plus 9,000 frontage-road miles. If all of the paved surface were brought together in a single square parking lot, it would hold two thirds of the vehicles operating in the United States. If all of the excavated fill were dumped on it, the state of Connecticut would be knee-deep in dirt. The sand, gravel, and crushed stone used in construction would build the Great Wall of China fifty times. The concrete used would build six sidewalks to the moon, and the tar and asphalt would provide driveways for thirty-five million ranch houses. Its lumber and timber requirements would leave treeless a 400-square-mile forest. The total culverts and drain pipes used would take care of Chicago's main water and sewage systems six times.

Yet the Interstate is biggest in cost. Its original price tag of a million dollars a mile was an arithmetical coincidence, since some stretches (inside metropolitan areas) cost several times as much as others ($18 million a mile for the downtown section of Detroit's Edsel Ford Expressway). And, of course, there are bridges, which can cost $1 million for 30 feet. But there are three important general points about the cost: First, the federal government's commitment of such huge sums over the space of a few years has been a significant contribution to the nation's prosperity, important enough so that long before the program is completed Washington economists are busy thinking up substitutes. Second, the numerous TV and magazine features purporting to expose scandal, graft, and corruption in the program were grossly off base. Any fair appraisal of the size of the job and the amount of graft that has actually been uncovered must produce a conclusion very favorable to the Bureau of Roads. When one recalls the wholesale robbing and jobbing that took place in connection with the construction of the transcontinental railroads, one cannot help realizing that we are living in a very different, very much better era. Third, and most important, the economic benefits of the Interstate Highway System are well established and extremely impressive. These merit a closer look.

The key economic question in second-half-of-twentieth-century America is that of growth. From whatever point of view one approaches economics, this is the great determinant. Growth means more prosperity, more leisure, more jobs, more security, and more taxes to pay the government's bills. Does the $47 billion spent on Interstate highways justify itself in terms of economic growth?

In the first place, the Interstate Highway System benefits business. Apart from the direct transport savings, highway-oriented relocation of industrial and other business establishments makes economies in operation possible. A plant can be situated in a place where there is enough room for it. Inventories do not have to be so large if more stock can be brought in quickly.

Farmers profit from it, too. With markets brought nearer, more advantageous use can be made of land, including more intensive cultivation, a wider choice of crops (because of the bigger market radius), and time advantages in harvesting and marketing by availability of migratory labor and harvesting equipment. Labor, too, finds improved job opportunities through increase in commuting radius.

Freeways and school buses make consolidated schools possible; public services are increased by the Highway System in many of the large areas with small populations of the West; this brings about important improvements in public services. Police and fire protection, mail delivery, library service, mobile X-ray units, visiting nurses, regional medical centers, and many others improve in efficiency.

Finally, freeways relieve urban congestion. If the automobile built the cities, it overdid the job. Every city in the

United States is congested. While alternate means of transportation promise the best long-range solution, the freeway development within metropolitan areas has been a lifesaver on a short-term basis. Many of the heaviest-traveled urban freeways are part of the Interstate System. The importance of this unlocking of congestion to midcity business can readily be appreciated. When imaginatively combined with urban-renewal projects—pedestrian malls, shopping centers, and cultural centers—the freeway, despite all the jokes about it, has already proved the city's best friend.

In the often bitter three-way argument among airlines, railroads, and trucking companies about who needs help the most and who is getting more than a fair share, one thing is unmistakable: the truck is still moving up in statistics of freight transport. In 1930, trucks hauled less than a twentieth of the freight per ton mile. Thirty years later, the truck proportion was a fifth—and a fifth of a far larger total. If the comparison is made on the basis of tonnage of commodities moved, leaving out distance, highways carry about half of the total; they carry over 60 percent of the farm products.

The automobile is no mere pleasure vehicle, even as a passenger carrier. Sixty-eight percent of all workers commute by auto, and among commercial passenger carriers, intercity buses account for 28 percent of total passenger miles.

All of these figures are projected upward, some of them dramatically, for the remaining years of this century. By 1975, there will be well over a hundred million motor vehicles operating. Herein lies ample justification for the $47 billion bill.

Aside from all economic imperatives, there is a benefit

built into the Interstate Highway System that must come
home to every driver. This is the safety factor. Ever since
the automobile made its appearance, it has wrought a constant, day and night, year-round havoc in America that can
only be compared to a war that never ends—thirty or forty
thousand dead and several hundred thousand casualties
every single year. It adds up to more slaughter than all our
wars, a statistic whose repetition has left us dully bemused.
Yet somehow or other we are at last beginning to get
automobile-safety conscious—witness the very tardy adoption of the seat belt.

From its inception, the Interstate Highway System was a
safety program. The very idea of long-distance, high-speed
travel prompts immediate consideration of safety. The
principal techniques embodied in the route design—access
control (the most important single feature), strong separation of opposing roadways, long-distance vision, antimo-
notony curves—are well known. In addition, there are
dozens of safety features built into shoulders, culverts,
bridge guards, and other details. How many lives will be
saved that would have been lost driving the same distance
on ordinary highways? On the basis of analysis of considerable experience, the Bureau of Roads estimates eight
thousand a year, a figure corroborated by independent
studies.

Some engineers have pointed out a very interesting historical parallel. At the end of the last century, intensive
campaigns were mounted against the carnage in the
factories—signs, slogans, exhortations, fines for careless-
ness, awards for safety, and so on. None of this helped.
Then a new approach was tried. The factories themselves
were engineered for safety. It was made easy, instead of

difficult, for a worker to run his machine without getting his hand or foot caught. Magically, the accident rate dropped off. In the same way, the endless campaigning of the National Safety Council and the press against highway speed has not caused motorists to slow down or accidents to decline. Now, with the Interstate System, a new approach is being tried. It is being made easy instead of difficult for a motorist to drive at high speeds without smashing his car up.

In view of the savings in human lives and crippling injuries and the rich economic benefits, the remaining cavil against the Interstate Highway System might be overlooked, but it deserves some attention because it is so misleading. This is the criticism—sometimes a grumble, sometimes a sneer—about the effect of these roads on the countryside. The rolling farm land, the evergreen forest, the lake-shore dunes, the wilderness—these American treasures are pictured as being eaten up by great obtrusive ribbons of concrete. It is not so. The size of the Interstate System must be put into perspective. Forty-one thousand miles is a lot of highway, but it represents only a minute fraction of the 3½ million-square-mile area of the United States, and most of it lies in already spoiled countryside. The damage to our natural wonders by the concrete alone is pretty evidently insignificant, and at least a reservation should be noted in favor of some elements of the Interstate highways—roadways skillfully wound around mountain slopes and bridges blended into their settings, for example —that can properly be said to enhance the scenic background.

What provokes the sneers and grumbles, one suspects, is not the concrete itself, but the fact that the concrete is covered with automobiles, and the automobiles filled with people. Once delightfully secluded beaches, parks, mountain trails, and trout streams are full of people now that the new section of expressway is in. Some of them litter, most of them bring children, all of them take up room. It's terrible.

Is it? Should the unspoiled parts of America be left unspoiled—and unenjoyed by most Americans—or should everybody be given a chance to visit the Rockies, the Pacific, the Adirondacks, the Ozarks, and the rest? The best answer, I believe, is that we should try hard to have it both ways. Keep as much of our beautiful country as we can unspoiled and at the same time be glad, not sorry, that the Interstate Highway System makes it possible for far more people to visit far more of it.

Sometimes, indisputably, there are real conflicts. For example, should California cut down giant redwoods to make room for an expressway? But the California-redwood type of controversy is rare in comparison with the miles of Interstate roads and rarer yet in comparison with the vacation miles per American family. A Detroiter can drive to the Michigan Upper Peninsula for a week-end fishing trip; a New Yorker can show his family the Mississippi; a Chicagoan can discover San Francisco; a Georgian couple can explore New England. There are some potential benefits here, too, that go much farther than vacation fun.

10
The Aswan Tames the Nile:
Sadd-el-Aali

"SOLDIERS," said Napoleon at the Battle of the Pyramids, "forty centuries look down on you." The Russian and Egyptian engineers who today are directing the mammoth complex of digging and construction that will be the Aswan Dam might well say something similar to their army of thirty thousand Arab workmen. Never was so tremendous an engineering work undertaken in the midst of so many of the treasures of a distant antiquity. Even the archaelogical treasures into which the Rome and Moscow subways have plowed are insignificant beside the breathtaking mass of Abu Simbel, the great temple, and the thousands of artifacts of every description from many ancient cultures that line both shores of the great river that is being harnessed for agriculture and industry.

This vast storehouse of the irreplaceable relics of history has attracted more attention than the dam itself. The earliest announcement of the dam brought cries of alarm from the world's archaeologists, for the huge barrier will back up the Nile into a 300-mile-long lake 300 feet deep, which will sink all the treasures of southern Egypt, Nubia, and the Sudan forever under water.

"It [the dam] will amputate a portion of our memories," says French archaeologist Georges Fradier. "To resign oneself to such a loss would mean accepting a kind of partial amnesia, like that of a man who has no memory of his early childhood or of his parents. It is quite possible that he may be happy without it. But we should pity him for . . . not knowing where he came from."

Of the countless imperiled treasures, one stands out. This is the gigantic cliff temple of Abu Simbel, carved from the Nubian rock by the architects of Seti I and his son Ramses II, great kings of the Nineteenth Dynasty (thirteenth century B.C.). Facing the west bank of the Nile sit four colossal statues of Ramses, three of which are nearly intact. They guard the portal through which one enters the interior of a temple whose ceiling is 100 feet above the floor. Some 200 yards to the north stands the smaller but still impressive temple of Nefertari, Ramses' beautiful queen. Rediscovered in 1815 by the Swiss traveler and explorer Johann Ludwig Burckhardt, Abu Simbel and its small sister were cleared of sand in 1817 and immediately became one of the world's most renowned archaeological wonders.

This historic monument will be saved from obliteration in a feat of engineering that may indeed overshadow the dam itself. By measures never before attempted on such a scale, the temples will be cut out of the mountain and then raised and reset in a new location.

"Modern Egypt is threatened with a human catastrophe," says a spokesman for the United Arab Republic. "The High Dam, no useless pyramid, is the cornerstone of the one solution which can turn this disaster, the exploding

population, into a triumph." Ninety-seven percent of
Egypt's surface is desert, and yet the population is increasing at such a rate that it will reach forty million by 1975.
Something must be done about that 97 percent of land
area. Two things, Egyptian scientists point out, can be
done. First, some of the desert can be turned into farm
land. Second, some of it can be used for industry. For the
first, irrigation is essential; for the second, power. The
Aswan Dam can supply both.

"Egypt is the gift of the Nile." This sentence from
Herodotus is the Greek student's first lesson. Third longest
of the world's rivers, its special characteristics distinguish
it sharply from the Plata and Mississippi Rivers, with their
far-ranging tributaries. The White Nile, rising in lakes
south of the equator 4,000 miles from the sea, flows slowly
northward for over 2,500 miles before it receives the
waters of the Blue Nile, which rises in the highlands of
Ethiopia to the east. Another 140 miles south it is joined by
its only other tributary, the Atbara.

The Blue Nile and the Atbara are a pair of freshets,
trickles that for a few weeks every spring turn into torrents.
At Khartoum, the river enters the tableland of Nubian
sandstone that underlies the Sahara. On the surface of this
vast plain, it turns eccentrically this way and that, reversing itself in a series of loops and hairpins that ultimately
bend southward in a great S. In six separate places, its
flow is interrupted by irregular masses of rock through
which in the long millennia it has not yet eroded a channel.
These are the celebrated cataracts of the Nile. Three of
them interrupt navigation on this otherwise highly naviga-
ble stream.

The northernmost (first) cataract marks the boundary

of ancient Egypt proper. Sixty-eight miles to the north the sandstone gives way to softer limestone through which the river long ago cut a deep valley, ranging from 10 to 30 miles wide. The floor of this valley is carpeted with the famed black alluvial mud, the "gift of the Nile," which made possible the civilization of the Pharaohs. Every spring the Nile flood, swollen by the torrents of the Blue Nile and the Atbara, roars over the six cataracts and pours in a wide belt down the valley to the broad triangular mouth, named by the Greeks the delta from its resemblance to the fourth letter of their alphabet. In the valley and in the Delta, through the New Stone Age, the people grew their crops and built their cities and monuments, inventing writing, mathematics, astronomy, and architecture as they progressed.

Yet the Nile's bounty had drawbacks with which the ancient Egyptians were unable to cope. Its floods were unequal. Some years the water rose too high, wiping out villages and drowning thousands; some years its flooding was too meager, and thousands perished of starvation. And always, a vast proportion of the annual torrent was wasted, rolling out to sea unused.

An effort was made at the turn of the twentieth century to deal with the problem of the Nile's uneven generosity. Egypt was then under a British administration whose principal interest was to provide a favorable political and economic climate for cotton growing and other European enterprises. It had long been realized that the river could be made to yield more benefits and fewer troubles if a dam were built in the neighborhood of the First Cataract, and in 1898 the first Aswan Dam was undertaken. It was equipped with 180 sluice gates through which the crest of the annual

flood could be passed. From the point of view of flood
control, this was a good solution, but aside from producing
no power, it also failed to utilize most of the torrent, which
was merely allowed to pass out to sea in an orderly
manner.

The new dam—Sadd-el-Aali, the High Dam—is an
Egyptian dream come true. It will not only transform agriculture but create almost from scratch a powerful modern
industry, based on a tremendous 2,100,000-kilowatt productive capacity (10 billion kilowatt-hours per year of
electric power). Twelve generating units, housed in six tunnels parallel to the riverbed, will equal sixty million Egyptians in labor power.

The backup lake—Lake Nasser—will be 311 miles
long, reaching up the Nile far into neighboring Sudan.
Lake Mead, the Hoover Dam's backup, the biggest man-
made reservoir in the United States, is only a fourth as
large, but Kariba Reservoir in Rhodesia and Bratsk Reservoir in Siberia are both larger. Lake Nasser will guarantee
Egyptian farmers a steady, day-in, day-out, year-round
flow of water for irrigation in flood years and in drought
years. The famed Nile flood will become a wonder and a
terror of the past.

Sadd-el-Aali will increase the national income by $500
million a year, a sum that not too long ago represented
Egypt's total.

Several preliminary studies had been carried out even
before Soviet aid for the project was settled. Ultimately,
the Russian and Egyptian engineers decided on a two-stage
project:

Stage one: Construction of cofferdams to block the
river above and below the dam site and a diversion canal,

including the power tunnels, to carry the river around the site. Also included in stage one is a giant spillway.

Stage two: Construction of the High Dam itself.

The cofferdams cannot provide dry land for working. The water is much too deep to be pumped out. This is because of the location of the old British-built dam, only 7

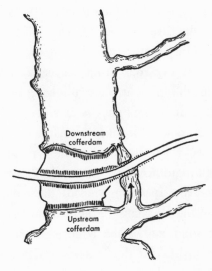

Plan of Aswan Dam, showing upstream and downstream coffer-dams, main dam, and diversion canal. Powerhouse is located be-tween arrows.

miles downstream; the High Dam must be built in the mid-dle of the water it backs up, 115 feet deep. The chief con-tractor, Ahmed Osman, and his Russian advisers figured that it would be too costly even to lower the river level much, so they elected to work in the deep water. The coffer-dams, however, performed an indispensable service—they shut off the current. The fill for the main dam could be neatly dumped into this still-water lagoon.

Preliminary work, access roads on both banks and a soil-research laboratory, was carried out in the late 1950's. On January 9, 1960, President Nasser laid the foundation stone, and the workshops, stores, compressed-air stations, explosive depots, barracks for engineers and workers, and other necessary buildings began going up. Russian power-shovels, bulldozers, dump trucks, excavators, and cranes began pouring in, and Egyptian drivers started using them to dig away at the diversion canal. This job was integrated with the cofferdam construction, the Russians trucking and barging loads of big rock from the canal trench to the cofferdam site, dumping it, and following up by sluicing the rock with a dune-sand-and-water slurry through pipes lowered near the embankment level. After filling the spaces between the rocks with the slurry, they piled more dune sand on, weighting down every 13 feet with a layer of rock placed against the upstream side of the cofferdam. This method is one the Russians developed on the Volga. The surcharge of sand makes the cofferdam more solid and stable, and supplies fill that automatically takes care of new voids that develop from water seeping through and consolidating the original sand. Completed in the autumn of 1964, the two cofferdams contained a solid 10 million cubic yards of material. Completion of the upstream cofferdam had the immediately valuable effect of increasing the volume of water stored by the old dam by some 4 billion cubic yards, later growing to 8 billion. This stored water was available for immediate use to reclaim 1¼ million acres of desert and convert another ¾ million acres from partial to complete irrigation.

The upstream cofferdam, whose function is to channel the river into the diversion canal, is 156 feet, considerably higher than the downstream cofferdam, which serves to keep the river from flowing back into its old bed after it emerges from the canal. The High Dam will incorporate both cofferdams

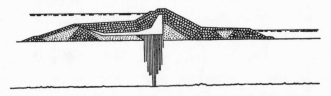

Cross section of the Aswan High Dam. The grout curtain extends down to bedrock to seal off seepage. Above it are layers of sand (dotted), rock (pebbled), and concrete and clay (white). Maximum upstream water level is at left.

The grout curtain under the center of the dam had to go down more than 600 feet in some places to hit bedrock and seal off seepage 100 percent.

The big spillway constructed on the western bank of the river has a wall 590 feet above sea level, the same height as the High Dam. Thus if the water gets high enough to go over the dam, it instead flows into the spillway, to be saved and rerouted later through the power tunnels on the east bank. Not a drop of Nile water will run to waste.

It is hard to think of an engineering project in all of history that has promised a greater social and economic impact. Here are some of the benefits forecast by Egyptian experts:

1. About 1¼ million acres of new farm land will be added and nearly another million acres will be converted from erratic "basin" irrigation to perennial irrigation. Water will be guaranteed even in drought years. Egypt's considerable rice crop will be an important beneficiary,

and long-overdue crop diversification will be made possible. Cane sugar production should increase from 300,000 to 500,000 tons.

2. Ten billion kilowatt hours a year of electric power will furnish at one tremendous stroke the basis for an industrial economy. In addition, the dam will insure a continuous head of water for other dams along the lower Nile, guaranteeing steady power production throughout the year. The old dam, downstream, will benefit enormously: the even flow will nearly double output of its own new hydroelectric station.

3. Flood control will end forever the periodic havoc wrought by the Nile through fifty centuries. The savings in levee maintenance alone will be important.

4. Better drainage will upgrade existing farm land throughout the valley.

5. Navigation on the vital waterways will become simpler.

Altogether, United Arab Republic experts calculate, the High Dam's economic benefits will exceed its total cost within two years after completion—another record hard to equal among the world's great engineering projects. Modern Egyptians contrast it with the benefits derived by ancient Egyptians who labored under the lash to build the great pyramids.

Aside from the advantages to the United Arab Republic, there will be important gains for Sudan, the newly independent developing country to the south. The cultivable area of Sudan will be multiplied threefold, with a corresponding increase in the government's revenues. This benefit is a *quid pro quo* for the backup of the river, which will drown the land of the Sudanese Nubians, ninety thousand people who have dwelt in the Nile Valley since prehistoric times, and who must now be moved to new homes in the valley of the Nile's eastern tributary, the Atbara. Egypt's own sixty thousand Nubians are already moving to new homes in the sugar-growing area north of Aswan.

Even archaeologists, who feared disaster, have turned the dam project into a benefit. The long-neglected upper Nile became the scene of the most intensive archaeological exploration ever carried out anywhere. The finds have been valuable and often totally unexpected. Hans Nordstrom, wandering over one of the tiny islets in the Second Cataract, noticed a crevice 15 feet above the water level: a Neolithic fishing camp, six thousand years old. Professor C. Michalowski, leader of a Polish expedition, found beautiful colored frescoes, as fresh as the day they were painted, on the walls of a thousand-year-old Christian church at Faras, an ancient Nubian village soon to be covered by Lake Nasser. Mrs. W. B. Emery, wife of the leader of the British Egyptian Exploration Society's expedition, walking her dog on the river bank, noticed something coppery in the sand—copper slag that led to a forty-six-hundred-year-old industrial town.

The relic that has captured most imaginations is Abu Simbel, the cavernous temple of Ramses. The rescue of this mighty work of art challenged the genius of the world's best engineers. One scheme after another was suggested.

Finally, in 1962, with zero hour approaching, the Swedish engineering firm of Vattenbyggnadsbyran (VBB) put forward a proposal prepared at the request of the Ministry of Culture and National Guidance in Cairo. It consisted of cutting the temples up, moving them piecemeal, and reassembling them on the new bank of the broadened river. VBB and several other firms in a consortium headed by Hochtief A.G. of Essen, Germany, embarked on a three-stage job. The first stage, just as in the building of Sadd-el-Aali, was a cofferdam, 1,200 feet long, constructed of 480,000 cubic yards of material and sealed with a steel sheetpile cutoff, which protected the temple from the 26-foot autumn rise in the river. Behind this barricade, the European-Egyptian crews launched stages two and three. Stage two is the excavation—in effect, removing a large segment of sandstone cliff above the temple. Explosives could not be used, lest they damage the temple below. Extraordinary measures had to be taken to protect the statues against the rockfalls from ordinary digging and cutting above. One hundred and twenty thousand pounds of fine, clean sand were packed around each of Ramses' four images with the care normally reserved for applying a mud pack to the face of an aging dowager.

Inside the temples, similar precautionary measures took the form of a dense network of steel centering. The excavation stops 33 feet above the temple ceiling, except in the rear and at the sides of the temple, where it cuts to below the level of the floor to free the huge edifice from the surrounding cliff.

During stage three, stonecutters chop the immense façades into blocks of 30 tons and the temple rooms into blocks of 20 tons without causing them to crack or crumble. The cuts, about ⅜ inch thick, are made where they will do the least harm, aesthetically, except where existing cracks, fissures, and weak zones in the natural rock dictate certain lines. The massive blocks, containing their precious hewn and ornamental surfaces in jigsaw form, must be drilled and fitted with vertical lifting bars, then hoisted to trucks and carried to the new site. Cracked, fissured, or weak rock is strengthened by drilling and injection of grout or resin before lifting.

The frescoed ceilings demand maximum care. They are being exposed to sunlight for the first time. Insurance coverage is elaborate, with some individual blocks of stone insured for millions of dollars, lest their truck ride, cushioned in white sand, damage them.

The most delicate part of the work is cutting up the four statues of Ramses. The sand embankment piled against the huge figures gives the stonecutters a scaffold, while protecting the statues as the work progresses.

At the re-erection, the joints between the sandstone blocks of the temple walls will be filled with mortar, and the blocks backfilled with reinforced concrete. Then the thousand blocks of the great temple will be hemmed with some five thousand smaller blocks cut from the surrounding rock surface at the old site. At last, the huge temple will stand above the new, broader Nile, as it did above the old for thirty-three centuries. And the immense stone Pharaohs will gaze once more at the rising sun, perhaps for another thirty-three centuries, before some new construction of man forces them to move again.

11
The Voice in the Sky:
From Telephones to Telstar

THE INTRODUCTION of the Early Bird synchronized satellite system, by which one may send one's voice 23,000 miles out into space and have it accurately returned to earth at some other point, is possibly the most remarkable of the succession of miracles that have marked the nine decades of telephone history. The first was the notion, conceived by a teacher of the deaf and successfully demonstrated with the help of an electrician's apprentice, that the human voice could be sent over an electric circuit. The second was the switchboard, which ingeniously transformed the Mr. Bell-to-Mr. Watson call into a network. Further miracles turned the switchboard into a massive and instantaneous mechanism capable of servicing calls by the thousand, while another set made it possible to transmit thousands of voices over a single package of wires or simply through the air, from one tower to the next, over hundreds of miles. The story was already fantastic before Telstar and Early Bird gave it their science-fiction turn.

Pick up your telephone, manipulate a few digits on the dial, and through an inconceivably complicated series of mechanical and/or electronic connections, plus one or two or more wires, cables, microwave towers, or satellites, and you are talking to your sister in Spokane, or to your firm's licensee in Tokyo, or to the *Queen Elizabeth* at sea. In the continental United States alone, there are hundreds of thousands of routes by which a phone call can travel from one point to another. Here is a sample, illustrating an actual call from a professor at Stanford to a business firm in Rochester, New York:

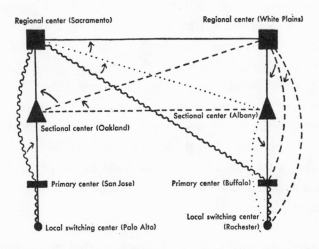

Possible routing for a phone call from Palo Alto, California, to Rochester, New York. The wavy line shows the fastest route.

The modern computer evolved from the telephone system, and one way of looking at the telephone network is to see it as a global-size computer, accurately juggling thousands of messages—not all phone calls, but TV, telephotos, and masses of business data coming off punched tape, magnetic tape, punched cards, drawings, and plain written words.

Early Bird, a repeating station in the sky, and Telstar, its experimental forebear which was also a laboratory, had to receive all this jumble of sounds and pictures, keep them sorted, and amplify them so they would be audible after the long trip back to earth. Quite a trick. To put it, and the switching system, into perspective, let us return a moment to Alexander Graham Bell and Tom Watson, in Boston in 1875. Following their historic one-line conversation ("Mr. Watson, come here, I want you!"), the inventor and his young helper set to work to raise money for development of Bell's invention. They gave a series of lectures. Watson, stationed two blocks from the lecture hall, sang "Hold the Fort for We Are Coming" and "Do Not Trust Him, Gentle Maiden" at the top of his lungs as a demonstration of the telephone's capabilities. The two men had to return to their workshop, for there were several wrinkles to be ironed out before the public's enthusiastic demand could be met. A bell had to be devised so that a telephone user could signal to the party at the other end. Then the instrument itself had to be improved in quality.

Bell's original telephone comprised both sender and receiver in the same instrument; you held it up to your mouth for talking and to your ear for listening. The waves created in the air by the speaker's voice were transmitted by the diaphragm to the electromagnet, which then sent out electrical waves with precisely the same pattern as the sound waves. How this happened was not fully understood by Bell or Watson or any of their contemporaries. In Bell's original instrument the current was controlled by sheer lung power—the rather insensitive diaphragm was only affected by great blasts of air. Farmers waiting in a country grocery store rushed out to hold their horses when they saw anyone preparing to use the telephone. Thomas A. Edison invented the transmitter used today—a chamber

full of carbon granules positioned behind the thin metal diaphragm whose vibration compacts the carbon granules and
increases the number of surfaces touching each other,
thus controlling the current.

The first telephones that Bell and Watson installed were
simple one-line, two-instrument affairs, connecting a house
and barn, or house and shop. As soon as they confronted
the real problem, that of installing telephone service in a
community, they ran into the question of switching. How
could several different subscribers pick each other out? A
simple signal bell would serve for several different stations
on one line—one crank for party one, two for party two, a
long and short crank for party three, and so on. But New
York could not be serviced that way. The answer lay in a
central office into which all the wires came, and where one
party's wire could be connected to another party's. This is
switching, and it is second in importance only to the original concept of varying electrical vibrations.

There was in existence a sort of primitive model of what
was required in the form of the telegraph signaling system.
This was used in large cities for messenger, fire, and police
calls. Signals came in to a central office and were taken
care of and recorded. There was no thought of a two-way
exchange between customers.

In May of 1877 in the office of E. T. Holmes of Boston, a
crude experimental switchboard was made to connect four
banks and a manufacturing concern. The five customers
could talk to each other during the day, and at night their
lines were plugged in to a burglar alarm. The next year the
first commercial switchboard was set up in New Haven.
Twenty-one telephone subscribers—on eight lines—were
connected to it.

Operator and subscribers alike were still armed with the single-unit transmitter-receiver. The operator received a visual signal on the board, connected his instrument with the appropriate line by plug, and listened while the caller requested his party. The operator then transferred the plug to the requested party's jack, completing the connection. As soon as regular service on a bigger scale was introduced, the process became more complicated.

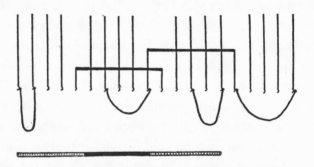

A nonmultiple switchboard. Three connections, one via a trunk line, are shown. Bars below represent two operators. Dotted lines show how far they can reach.

The original operators, incidentally, were male—boys and young men—and they were a defective element in the system. They talked back to subscribers, made too much noise, and carved their initials on the switchboard panels. Their replacement by young women was another landmark in improving the service, for the young women proved to be quiet, courteous, efficient, and patient with erring subscribers.

The number of telephones multiplied as fast as the instruments, switchboards, and cables could be manufactured. No sales force had to go on the road with the telephone. The problem was simply meeting the overwhelming market demand.

There was, of course, a limit to the number of lines a single operator could service. Large central offices had a giant board with thousands of jacks, requiring a whole crew of operators. Each subscriber's line had connections with the board at several different points so that the first operator not busy could answer an incoming call.

There was also a limit to the number of lines that could conveniently be handled in a single office, and by 1900, large cities were splitting the office in two, interconnecting by *trunk lines,* many wires in a bunch. A subscriber gave the local operator the number he wanted, and if it was outside the area handled by that exchange, she called the neighboring central office, repeated the number, and made the connection via the trunk line.

The young lady known as "Central" was enjoying her heyday, but a revolution was under way to supplant her. The trouble was mainly that operators could not be numerous enough to handle all the traffic, though there were also complaints about the fact that they were human. The human frailty of one switchboard operator, in fact, provoked the revolution. This was back in 1889, and it happened in Kansas City. An undertaker named Almon B. Strowger subscribed to the newfangled service and was presently outraged to find that prospective clients who gave the operator his number were being routed instead to one of his competitors. Investigation disclosed that the competitor's wife was a switchboard operator. Strowger's revenge was devastating. He produced an invention that eliminated telephone operators. He did it with a collar box and a handful of pins, out of which he constructed a model of a mechanical switching system. He stuck ten pins in a curving row on the inside of the round collar box, their heads protruding toward the center. He then pivoted a central arm so that it would make contact with each pin in turn as it rotated. Strowger patented his invention in 1891, and it was first installed in La Porte, Indiana, the following year.

An improved version of the Strowger switch is still in use today. It consists of ten rows of ten sets of contacts, each row arranged in an arc, just as in the original collar-box model. Two motions of the contact arm—one vertical, to find a selected row, the other rotary, to find a selected contact in that row—can connect it to any one of a hundred lines. The switch is driven by electromagnets and ratchet mechanisms.

In the original Strowger system, each telephone was equipped with three push buttons, one for each of three electromagnets in the switch, the first of which positioned

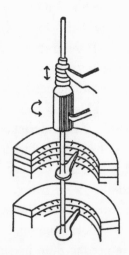

Simplified Strowger switch. The system is based on two motions of the contact arm—one vertical, to find a selected row, and the other rotary, to make a contact in that row.

the contact arm vertically, the second, in the rotary direction, and the third, back to the starting point. Using the three buttons a subscriber could set up his own direct connection with ninety-nine other phones. Technically, it was known as a *step-by-step system*, and still is, but popularly, as "the girl-less, cussless telephone."

The next major advance was the solution of the problem of trunk-line connections—in effect, allowing the subscriber to plug himself into an available trunk line connecting one central office to another, and then to select and ring the line for the telephone he is calling. This required participation of the switching network itself in the selection of a route—the secret behind the dial telephone. The subscriber dials a digit, causing the contact arm to select a particular row of contacts as before, but this row of contacts is a bank of trunk lines along which the contact arm searches automatically for a free one. The subscriber is now connected to the group of switches serving the number he is dialing, and his further dialing pulses operate these switches to make the proper connection. An average step-by-step dial office, the system described

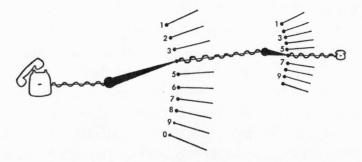

How step-by-step telephone dialing works. With two digits the caller can reach 100 phones. Here he has dialed 4, 6.

above, can serve up to ten thousand lines. It has about seventy thousand relays, each a combination of an electro-magnet and switch. When fed current, the electromagnet either closes a switch normally open or opens one normally closed.

To reach the hundred phones in this exchange, the caller must dial only two digits. A third digit makes it a thousand-phone network, and so on. Theoretically, the multiplication of switches and connections might be carried to infinity, but a finite limit is fixed by the shortcomings of the decimal system of numbers and the limits of a dial face. If more than the ten digits were put on a dial, people would be confused.

Step-by-step switching went into general use in the Bell System around 1919. Panel systems with motor-driven shafts considerably heightened the efficiency of the switch-ing in cities with complex switching problems. A further refinement in electromechanical switching was the develop-ment of the *crossbar switch,* first installed in 1938. This technique has been compared to a railroad switching yard where a dispatcher receives a call to send a train through the yard, and must plot a path through momentarily clear tracks.

The crossbar switch is a rectangular box with a lattice-work of vertical and horizontal bars. At each intersection is a relay-type contact called a *crosspoint.* To close a set of crosspoints and thereby complete a connection through a switch, a horizontal bar and then a vertical bar move.

Ten electrical paths can be plotted at once on such a switch, as compared with only one on a step-by-step. Here is how multiple paths can be set up in a crossbar switching network:

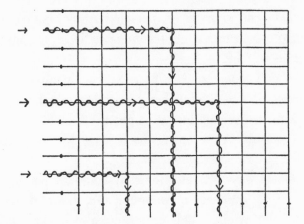

Three connections (wavy lines) made on a crossbar switch. Bars move horizontally and vertically until they meet at crosspoints. Equipment is released as soon as the connection is made.

The key advantage of crossbar switching is that the equipment is released as soon as a connection is made; it does not need to remain locked for the duration of a call. It effectively solves the problem of quick and precise switching on an enormous scale. Yet it too is being replaced. An electronic system based on numerical information processors using transistors acts with lightning speed, because information is stored in magnetic "memories" rather than by arrangements of wires and electromechanical equipment.

Electronic switching carries with it striking improvements in telephone service:

Abbreviated dialing. Frequently called local or long-distance numbers can be reached by dialing two to four digits instead of the usual seven or ten.

Dial conference. A caller can set up a three- or four-way telephone conversation by dialing each number in turn.

Add on. A third party can be brought into a conversation in progress.

Variable-call transfer. A person visiting another office or home can transfer all incoming calls to the number where he will be.

Fixed-call transfer. A subscriber can arrange for all incoming calls to be switched to another telephone when there is no answer on the called phone.

Call waiting. A customer who is using his telephone is signaled that another call is waiting.

In many ways the electronic system will be, like its forebears, a quicker, more automatic, more capacious form of the original Bell central-office switchboard. The basic idea goes back to the first days—all calls must be collected at a central point, switched, and sent out.

The telephone system consists essentially of three elements: the instrument, the switch, and the carrier. We are accustomed to think of the carrier as a wire, but this is far from being necessarily the case, especially in long-distance telephoning. The volume of long-distance calling today is growing at a rate reminiscent of the growth of local service in the first years. To accommodate all the long-distance traffic inside the United States on wires would be out of the question.

Alexander Graham Bell invented the telephone in an interval between bouts with a frustrating device he called a "harmonic telegraph." This idea was rooted in the fact that more than one message can be sent at a time over a single wire, something of obvious importance in the economical development of the early telephone. How many conversations can be carried at once over a single wire? None, actually, because the current in a single wire is all going one way, so two people talking to each other require two wires, one for each direction. But the single pair of wires can now carry sixteen conversations at once.

This fairly amazing trick is accomplished by *modulating* currents of different frequencies, that is, making the electrons in the different conversations dance to different times. Of course if more wires are added, more electrons are carried, and there was a time when American cities were festooned with an ever-expanding forest of overhead wires. Then came the cable that carried a bundle of wires, and then the *coaxial cable.* Famous largely because it carried early television programs (a use now virtually ended), the coaxial cable is really an enormous telephone wire. A copper wire is insulated inside a pencil-thick metal tube by washers. A pair of tubes forming a coaxial line, with the latest carrier system, can transmit 32,400 voice channels or a combination of voice and TV shows or data. Eight to twenty such pairs, enclosed in polyethylene sheathing, form a coaxial cable.

Another way to carry telephone and TV volume is the *radio relay.* The radio waves used as telephone carriers are of very short wavelengths, called *microwaves,* that travel in absolutely straight lines, not following the earth's curvature. They are beamed along from one tower to another about 30 miles away, in line of sight, like so many invisible searchlight beams. The valuable feature of microwave systems is their very short wavelengths, which permit each beam to be subdivided into a number of communications channels. Each of these channels in turn is usually capable of subdivision into 480 to 1,800 telephone circuits. Or, each channel can transmit a television program. One type of microwave carrier handles seventeen thousand phone conversations at once, or twelve TV programs going one way.

If microwaves are not intercepted by another tower, they keep right on going over the horizon, into the upper atmosphere, or troposphere. At this point something happens that proves of use to communications. Some of the waves are bent back to the earth, around the horizon in the direction of a receiving antenna hundreds of miles away. Over-the-horizon transmission requires huge and costly antennas that look like outdoor-movie screens. The received signal is also weak, but that is a small matter—it can be amplified and sent on to its destination or the next station by the same method or transferred to microwave relay. This method of transmission is useful in locations where it is not possible to place relay stations every 20 or 40 miles.

Still another extremely important long-distance carrier has been surprisingly tardy in development. Considering that Cyrus Field succeeded in laying his telegraph cable back in 1867, it is a little startling to find that a telephone cable was not laid across the Atlantic until 1956. The trouble was that a telephone conversation, unlike the less-complicated Morse code signal, needed amplification many times en route. Placing amplifier stations under the ocean was not an impossible problem from the engineering point of view, but in a cost sense it began to be worth while only in the 1950's. Transatlantic calls were made as early as the 1920's by radio, first longwave, then shortwave, but radio was subject to too much atmospheric interference to be consistently reliable. The undersea cable made a New York to London call no different than a New York to Brooklyn call. Today, there is a rapidly growing network of telephone undersea cables.

Undersea cables, over-the-horizon propagation, high-frequency radio, coaxial cables—all these seem like enough. They are not. The demand for telephone (and television) transmission across the Atlantic and Pacific is

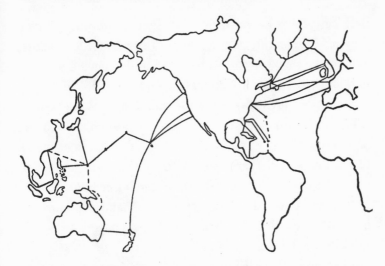

The first telephone cable across the Atlantic was not laid until 1956. Since then there has been a rapid expansion of undersea cables. The map shows existing cables and those planned for the future.

growing at about 20 percent a year, that is, doubling every 3 years, 9 months, and 18 days. Here we uncover the motive for the fabled Telstar experiment, which caught the imagination of the world. In the context of the telephone's history, Telstar is one more astonishing but logical development.

The Space Age has been popularly dated from the autumn of 1957, when the world suddenly blinked at the Russian Sputnik, the first satellite in the sky, but earth-orbiting satellites were a familiar concept among scientists long before 1957. Several proposals for using the well-known, and to a certain extent well-tested, theories behind the orbiting satellite had been made before Sputnik. Some were made in science-fiction stories, including one by the British author Arthur C. Clarke and another by Dr. John R. Pierce of

Bell Telephone Laboratories. Dr. Pierce also put his idea forward in scientific papers, but it drew very little attention outside the scientific community. Sputnik changed all that. Suddenly there was a National Aeronautics and Space Administration (NASA) with the mission of launching a whole galaxy of satellites. One was a big aluminum-coated balloon designed to study the effects of space phenomena of various kinds. Pierce seized the opportunity to suggest using the balloon as a passive reflector for communication. Echo was launched in August of 1960, and a microwave beam that carried the first telephone conversations via satellite was bounced off it.

Echo was a fragile little moon not designed to last, and its performance in any case was more a stunt than an engineering advance. The distance was too great for a reliable bounce operation, and there was too much interference. What was really needed, and what Pierce had in mind, was a satellite that would not passively reflect but actively amplify a signal. This was the idea behind Telstar.

Bell engineers had several valuable working tools at hand: the transistor, developed at Bell Labs, and its solid-state cousin the solar cell; the maser; the traveling-wave tube, the FM feedback receiver, and the horn-reflector antenna, built at Holmdel, New Jersey to track Echo. In a hill-ringed circle of woods near Andover, Maine, a horn with an aperture surface nine times as big as Echo's was built, which meant the whole structure, movable on both horizontal and vertical axes, was twenty-seven times as big. The horn had to be large enough to compensate for Telstar's tininess. The little satellite—little because the Thor-Delta rocket of 1960 couldn't lift much—was armed with only 2¼ watts of power. The feebleness of Telstar's signal had to be compensated for by a combination of power and precision on the ground. One antenna at Andover was designed to catch hold of Telstar in a general sort of way on the first pass, a second antenna to take over and lock on with greater precision, feeding the data on the satellite's track to a computer, which in turn would feed the data to the servomechanism moving the big horn.

Telstar, though small, was a tight little bundle of technologics, its heart a traveling-wave tube only a foot long but capable of amplifying a signal ten thousand times. Together with other components, it could amplify ten billion times. A solar-cell plant supplied operating energy. Command and telemetry systems, to turn off circuits when not operating and to monitor the general health of the little satellite, were crowded in.

In the gray predawn of July 10, 1962, the countdown at Canaveral went into its last moments. Zero . . . and the booster's huge flame sent the three-stage giant straight up, first slowly, then gathering momentum and arching into trajectory. The control room was filled with the tension of expectancy and apprehension. Far to the north, in the circle of wooded hills at Andover, another group waited with similar hopes and fears. In its early orbits, the satellite would not be visible. At last, two and a half hours after launching, on its fifth orbit, and almost precisely where predicted, Telstar came over the horizon. That night the American flag in the breeze in front of the radome at Andover appeared on European television screens.

For the next four months, Telstar continued to beam telephone messages and television between America and Europe. Then difficulties developed in its command decoders, and it failed to accept commands from the ground to shut off its receiver. This trouble was diagnosed as lying in certain transistors in the decoders, which, Bell engineers theorized, had received radiation damage from the Van Allen belts, through which the satellite constantly passed and repassed. A trick command signal was used to check the diagnosis. It was confirmed. Voltage was then successfully removed from the transistors, and the satellite functioned normally until mid-February of 1963, when it again went silent. For several more months, the capsule continued to whip about in its old orbit, following the earth around the sun along with several hundred other pieces of the debris of the Space Age. Its achievement was a chapter of history.

That history rapidly unfolded. It should be remembered that it had already begun before Telstar. Besides Bell, RCA and other private corporations were interested in satellite communications, and the Defense Department was very much interested. Two communications satellites, Score and Courier I-B, had spent a total of thirty days operating, and another, Courier I-A, had cracked up going off the launching pad. Telstar I's brilliant success was followed by the launching, late in 1962, of Relay I, a NASA satellite designed and built by RCA, which sent TV, voice, and various other transmissions not only between the United States and Europe, but between the United States and South America, and between the United States and Japan. Relay I was followed early in 1964 by Relay II, as Telstar I had already been followed by Telstar II in the spring of 1963. Both were simply improved versions of their forerunners.

Now something really different was coming up—or going up. If a satellite 600 to 6,000 miles high can connect the eastern United States to western Europe, what does it

take to connect the whole world together by satellite telephone? There were two ways it could be done. A profusion
of Telstars, zipping back and forth around the world, orbits
constantly altering, could cover the whole globe. At any
given time, a telephone subscriber could find at least one of
them within range. On the other hand, what would be the
minimum of satellites that could theoretically keep the
whole globe in sight? The answer is three, if they are
positioned over the equator and if they are moving at a
speed that just enables them to keep abreast of a given point
on the earth's rotating surface. Actually, it might be two,
but that would put them far up, and the height required
of three, almost 23,000 miles, already poses a rather
unexpected problem—that of the slowness of light: In
the give-and-take of conversations, can people learn to
wait for their voices to travel some 45,000 miles up
and down, plus ground-level distance, before talking
back to each other? Some of the early experiments were
disastrous on this count.

The orbit of a *synchronous satellite* is very unlike that of
most satellites. While Telstar, Sputnik, Explorer, and the
rest whip around the earth in a sort of slingshot motion,
going far out and then coming close, the synchronous satellite must keep a uniform altitude. This is a matter of speed.
A satellite fired into an elliptical orbit can be accelerated
into a circular one by firing another rocket.

The first test of this synchronous type of satellite came in
early 1963 when Syncom, built by Hughes Aircraft for
NASA, was sent up. It went into a pretty good orbit, 21,268
miles to 22,974 miles, but its communication system failed
at the outset. Syncom II, launched the following July,
achieved an even better (more nearly circular) orbit, and
transmitted steadily.

Though the Defense Department preferred the "random" system embodied in a great number of Telstars because it was less easily jammed, the successful launch of Early Bird in April, 1965, gave the synchronous satellite a commanding lead in the race to communications by way of space. The Communications Satellite Corporation (Comsat), authorized by Congress but under private ownership, orbited this first satellite designed for commercial, not experimental, purposes. The mission of Early Bird I was to establish regular telephone and TV communication with Europe. Two more Early Birds awaited launching. The three, hanging in the sky not like earth satellites but like the changeless stars, are the newest wave in the ninety-year succession of telephone miracles.

Millions of conversations, covering everything from global diplomacy to hotel reservations, will wing 23,000 miles out into space and come back down again at their destinations in London, Calcutta, or Houston, and with the general extension of the already proven Picturephone, we will be able to send our faces as well as our voices to any point on the earth's surface. Alexander Graham Bell would have been pleased. Not too surprised, perhaps, but pleased.

12
Hell Hole:
Launching the Titan Missile

MOST ENGINEERING CONCEPTS revolve around utility and cost. The more you spend to build something, the more use you hope to get out of it. The exception that proves this rule is a complicated hole in the ground in Colorado that cost a lot of money and that everyone connected with is very glad to see has never been used at all. If its companion and successor holes in the ground in South Dakota, Montana, Washington, Idaho, Wyoming, Arizona, and Arkansas remain equally unused, everybody will be really happy.

Had the Titan launch complex at Lowry Air Force Base, Colorado, gone into action during its four years of life, it would have meant that New York, Chicago, Los Angeles, and most of the other cities of the United States had just been wiped out in rolling flashes of hell-fire.

Much has been learned about building hardened sites since 1958 when work on the Titan complex began. Minuteman, the new solid-fuel missile, has been housed with little difficulty, partly because its launch characteristics make it easier to nest, and partly because its predecessor, Titan, supplied the experience. But in the winter of 1957–1958 nobody really knew how to build a *hardened site*—a hole in the ground in which a missile, its fuel, its support elements, and its command crew could be made proof against a near miss by a multimegaton H bomb. The idea, of course, was to give the United States a *second-strike capability*—the capacity to absorb a nuclear attack and then hit back effectively.

This is a much more complicated problem than it may seem at first glance. The Titan missile had to be elevated aboveground and fueled in order to fire, which is not true of the Minuteman. Part of the Titan's fuel element was *LOX,* liquid oxygen, which cannot be left in the missile but must be drained and stored after each alert. Also, the Titan was a *radio-inertial* guided missile—the power stage of its flight had to be controlled from the launch site. Therefore an antenna was needed, which had to lock onto the guidance mechanism of the missile just before launching. To do this, the antenna had to be elevated aboveground along with the missile itself and then lowered back into its silo. In the midst of Armageddon, how could you be sure it would still be there to be lowered and so ready to launch the next Titan?

The missile had to be kept under strict temperature and humidity control inside its silo. Machinery and power had to be provided to open the silo doors and raise the 110-ton Titan to launch position. The electronic facilities of the control center, plus lighting, heat, and other requirements, added up to the power needs of a town of five thousand for each Titan complex, a complex consisting of three missiles and their support facilities. All of the instruments and machinery, the Air Force ruled, had to be able to reduce the *overpressure* of a near-miss to an acceleration of 3 g's. That is, everything in the complex, large and small, had to be so protected and mounted that an H-bomb blast close by would only apply a pressure of three times gravity.

In February of 1958, the whole problem was placed
squarely on the desks of the engineers belonging to a joint
venture named Architect-Engineer for the first operational
ICBM squadrons at Lowry Air Force Base, Denver. The
joint venture was headed by Daniel, Mann, Johnson, and
Mendenhall of Los Angeles, associated with Leo A. Daly
Company of Omaha and Mason and Hanger—Silas Mason
of New York and the Rust Engineering Company of Pittsburgh. The Air Force's Senior Panel of Engineering Con-
sultants supplied a valuable theoretical first step by analyz-
ing seismic data gathered from earthquakes and evaluating
them as they might apply in a nuclear blast.

The Architect-Engineer group took these evaluations and
tried to figure out how to reduce the pressures on Diesel
engines, transistors, switching gear, pumps, valves, and everything else to 3 g's. They came up with a three-stage
system of shock absorption. The exterior walls of the missile silos, the antenna silos, the powerhouse dome, the
connecting tunnels, and the rest of the complex were designated Shock Zone A. Items mounted directly to these would
be subject to a maximum acceleration of 50 g's—50 times
their own weight. Inside the missile silo would be a crib,
cradling the Titan in a flexible embrace. This was Shock
Zone B. Finally, the floor of the silo would be *shock
mounted*—balanced on giant springs. This was Shock Zone
C. The total effect would be to reduce the acceleration to
the required 3 g's. Similar three-stage measures did the
same job for the other elements.

Here is how the three-stage shock mounting works out in
detail inside the missile silo. First, a 161-foot-deep cylindrical hole was dug and lined with reinforced concrete, 2
feet thick for most of the shaft's depth but coning out to-

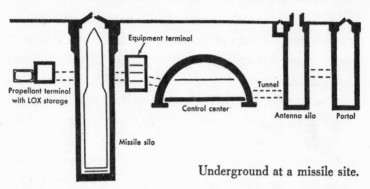

Underground at a missile site.

ward the top to a thickness of 13 feet 9 inches. On top was a double-leaf hinged silo door, each leaf 42 inches thick and weighing 116 tons. These doors, atop the tapering concrete thickness of the silo lining, can withstand a vertical load of 50 million pounds. Below, the silo was made to stand on a base slab 8 feet thick.

So much for Zone A. Inside the lining is the shock mounting of Zone B, a steel crib weighing 480 tons, supported on eight giant spring shock mounts imbedded in the concrete wall. The springs are coiled steel, 3 inches thick. Finally, Shock Zone C: all the electrical and mechanical connections and piping in the silo were made flexible so they could ride with the missile's motions.

Throughout the complex, the same pattern was repeated by the excavating, concreting, and steelworking crews—a deep hole, thick concrete lining tapering up, coiled steel springs and spring beams supporting floors and major pieces of equipment, flexible connections and piping.

Besides the three missile silos at the Lowry complex, there are propellant and equipment terminals, a powerhouse, antenna terminals and silos, a control center, the main portal, and the connecting tunnels. Basically these are much like the missile silos, though differently shaped

and not so deeply buried. The powerhouse is the most interesting from the engineering standpoint. A hemispherical
dome was picked as the most appropriate blast-resistant
form. A dome is not a good place to house Diesel engines,
because it heightens the noise. Sound-absorbent wall lin-
ings were installed to damp down the racket, though men
who have worked in the powerhouse say they can still hear
the engines even though they plug their ears.

Though the powerhouse itself is not nearly as deep as the
missile silo, it includes water wells, some going down 1,200
feet. The dome, 123 feet in diameter, has two floor levels,
both shock mounted on spring beams, and the four genera-
tors (three working, one stand-by) are mounted on their
own coil springs.

There are two antenna silos, one housing a stand-by,
which is the logical answer to the problem posed by the
need to leave the antenna above ground for several minutes
following launch.

The control center, with whose dial-studded consoles and
war clocks every moviegoer and magazine reader is familiar, is actually very similar in construction to the powerhouse. It is a 100-foot-wide dome, with two levels mounted
on spring beams. Here arose a problem outside the scope
of the Architect-Engineer. The shock mountings reduced
the acceleration danger to 3 g's all right. But can delicate
electronic equipment take a force of 3 g's? In 1958, electronics manufacturers simply did not know. A major test
program had to be carried out on a crash basis to find out.
Some of the components had to be fitted with special
mountings of their own.

The connecting tunnels have an unusual kind of shock
lining—steel plate with asbestos-impregnated asphalt. The

portal silo, entrance to the whole complex, is 75 feet deep
and very wide—29½ feet—because it must house a 10-ton
freight elevator. Like the control center, the portal, with its
heavy blast doors and its closed-circuit TV screen, checks
out everybody coming in. The blast doors at the Vandenberg Test Facility in California, built by the same engineering combine at the same time as Lowry, got a genuine
test one day in 1960. A fully loaded missile (with a
dummy warhead) was being lowered into the silo when the
supporting rig gave way and the missile slammed down to
the bottom, causing a considerable explosion. The missile
silo, equipment terminal, and propellant terminal—in order
words, the whole "launcher"—were knocked out completely, but the blast doors in the connecting tunnel held,
and no further damage resulted.

What is a working day like in Hell Hole? Imagine you
are a missile combat-crew member—a noncom specialist or
an officer, ranks running rather high in this service, in the
724th Strategic Missile Squadron. You arrive for work in a
fairly undramatic way, by bus. You stop briefly before a
cyclone fence where a sentry checks you in and proceed to
a spot where a domed manhole sits inconspicuously in the
tall grass. This covers the portal. It swings open in response
to a signal that the Air Force has not released, and you and
your buddies on the shift step inside and descend a narrow
spiral ladder. At its foot, you are confronted by a massive
steel door. As you stand there you are scanned by a TV
camera monitored down at control. If it turns out you are
O.K., you can turn the handle; give a shove to get it
started, and the giant door slowly revolves, a huge cylinder
carrying you with it, and deposits you within.

Inside, the freight elevator is directly in front of you, but you use the stairs down to the tunnel, well lighted but rather narrow, pipes and cable conduits on either side. The whole place is a bit of a tight fit, and amid all the grotesque explosive power you develop a healthy concern over bumping your head.

Whichever part of the complex you are assigned to, your first stop is the lower level of the control center for briefing. Then you go, with your buddy (nobody does anything alone at a missile site), either up a short flight of stairs to the console-lined control room, down a short tunnel to the powerhouse, or down a long one to either the antenna silo or one of the launchers. Whichever it is, they all have certain features in common. If your job is sedentary, it is not quite like being in an office on Park Avenue—you are strapped in by a seat belt. If you are working in the powerhouse, you have ear plugs.

In the control center, commands in code are received by a loud-speaker, and the day's exercise, whatever it is, is begun. Tape recorders take down every code signal, every telephone buzz, every word of command. When the exercise includes a practice launch order, everybody moves fast. This goes especially for the men on maintenance in the missile silos, who clamber out, double-time, down the tunnel, and secure the blast doors. The loading and lifting of the missile is done automatically on command from the control center. On the prairie above, one by one, three white noses emerge. At the opposite end of the complex, the disk-shaped antenna, wrapped in a weatherproof bag, also pokes up into the air.

Briefly, the three missiles and the antenna dominate the landscape; then they slowly retreat back into their nests. And now you and your buddy go to the mess hall, which is the same as the briefing room, the lower level of the control center, for chow.

Titan is now out of date. Only six Titan I and II squadrons were ever sited, each with three complexes of three missiles each—a total of fifty-four missiles. Minuteman, smaller and better because it is solid fueled, is well up in the hundreds and heading toward a programmed one thousand. Life in a Minuteman site is a little different from life in a Titan site. For instance, you probably arrive at your office by truck or helicopter, which makes you less like a civilian commuter. On the other hand, you are likely to be carrying a briefcase, because Minuteman is a more dispersed weapon, and the officers responsible for firing it check at operational headquarters before reporting to their command capsules. These are essentially like the Titan control center, except that each commands ten missiles, and each is manned by just two officers. Because of the Minuteman's solid fuel, it does not need to be fueled before flight; therefore, it does not need to be given launch exercises. (It is always ready, which is why it was given the name it has.) Consequently, ten of these missiles can be commanded by two men. Actually, hundreds of them could be commanded by one man, but the Air Force decided ten per two-man team would be enough. Why two men? Well, just in case one of them goes crazy, as in *Dr. Strangelove*. It takes both their keys to launch, and it also takes simultaneous "launch votes" from another squadron capsule to initiate launch. A single launch officer could not do anything about his colleague's key because both keys have to be turned at the same time and the two keyholes are many feet apart.

Without the endless launch exercises, life threatened to

be fearfully dull for Minuteman officers (all volunteers), so the Air Force thoughtfully assigned them all to study for undergraduate or advanced degrees in aerospace engineering and other subjects. One studies his calculus while his buddy watches the console in case a light flashes on and a tape recorder reports that the temperature has dropped a degree too low in No. 7, and maintenance men should check X conduit. The Minuteman silos, even more than the Titan ones, are, in the words of one visitor, "marvels of automation."

When one reflects on such construction details as the fact that a survey was made to check effects of gamma rays on plastic electronics components and that the powerhouse is designed to supply two weeks' power to the complex after cutoff of fuel, one finds it difficult to concentrate one's attention exclusively on the remarkable construction accomplishment of that first Titan base.

We now know that Stephen Vincent Benét's story about the neo-Indian boy stumbling on post-holocaust New York was wide of the mark. Post-holocaust New York will not be a mass of picturesque ruins—it will not be anything describable or recognizable. The more time goes by, the bigger the megatons get; and the more numerous the Minutemen and their Russian cousins grow, the more inevitably the same thing applies to cities, towns, and crossroads of diminishing size. Will the underground complex, with its beautifully efficient machinery so painstakingly mounted on springs, be the Stonehenge of America?

If technology—that is, science and engineering—has not brought us to this pass, it certainly has helped. Can it possibly suggest a way out? It can, and one may venture a bet that if we get out it will be more thanks to technology than to the art of politics. A look at one more wonder of the modern world may suggest a route by which science and engineering may "out of this nettle danger, pluck this flower safety."

13
An Automatic World?
Ford's Engine Plant No. 2

"The ability to build automated equipment . . . is almost unlimited."   THOMAS WATSON, JR., HEAD OF IBM

"The moment of truth on automation is coming a lot sooner than most people realize."
    AN EXECUTIVE OF THE RAND CORPORATION

"What I ha' seen since ocean steam began
Leaves me na doot for the machine: but what about the man?   RUDYARD KIPLING

ONE DAY in 1946, D. S. Harder, executive vice-president of the Ford Motor Company, thought up a new word—*automation*. Harder felt that a new word was called for to describe a significant improvement in production technique that the Ford Company was introducing—automatic materials-handling. Ford production lines were already mechanized: The operator introduced a part, pressed a button, and the machine did the rest. But the part had to be moved to the machine by separate mechanical and manual control, turned this way or that, and then moved on to the next machine. The portentous innovation of 1946 was only an overhead carrier. It extracted the work from the first machine, carried it to the second, and—the key step—

oriented it and fed it to the second machine without manual assistance. Given a system of such materials-moving devices, a whole sequence of operations could be rendered automatic. Human intervention became unnecessary.

The next step was obvious and was soon taken by Ford—a fully automatic factory. In September, 1950, a new stamping plant went into operation in Buffalo, and the following year a foundry and an engine plant were opened in Brookpark Village, Ohio, outside of Cleveland. All were fully automated—that is, the workpieces were fed, worked on, moved, oriented, fed, worked on, and so on, until finished by an almost wholly automatic process.

Four years later, in February 1955, Cleveland Engine Plant No. 2 was opened by Ford. It was a huge success. Between them, the two Cleveland plants soon were turning out well over a million V-8 and six-cylinder engines a year —more than half the number used by the whole Ford line, and about a sixth of the engines in all United States cars.

Seen from the outside, Engine Plant No. 2 is a large, trim, modern building. Unless you are looking at it from the air, you are deceived about its size until you enter, and then you are awed. Five football games could be played inside the vast space. That is, they could if there were nothing in the way, but so crammed is the space with machinery that one visitor could only express his reaction by saying he felt as if he had been suddenly reduced to pygmy size and had stepped into the interior of a single large machine.

Contrary to what one might expect, there are quite a few workers on the floor of Engine Plant No. 2. This is true also of the Westinghouse transformer plant in Athens, Georgia, the Goodyear-Gulf synthetic rubber plant in Neches, Texas, and a host of automated packaging, canning, manufacturing, and other plants throughout the nation. Engine Plant No. 2 is an example of *Detroit automation*—the connecting together of more or less conventional machines by transfer devices. It performs an extensive and complicated manufacturing process very efficiently, but it does not control itself. If a drill bores holes too deep, a human operator must take notice of gauge warnings, stop the machinery, and readjust the drill. Automation of the plant is by no means complete, and its distinctive feature is not the scarcity of personnel but the quantity of machinery. And what machinery! It does what men cannot do.

Six- and eight-cylinder engine blocks are transferred from one machine to the next without a workman moving a muscle. Camshafts move in files like marching soldiers from station to station, suspended from an overhead monorail that automatically feeds them into the proper machines. Arms of steel tilt engine blocks to any position in response to the turn of a crank, and hold them steady while manual jobs, such as installation of push rods and rocker arms, are performed. Heavy human labor, once the characteristic feature of an automobile plant, has been virtually eliminated.

Not all the advantages of this setup are immediately apparent. Quality control is such a one. Automatic nut running and bolt tightening, for example, achieve more uniform torquing than can be gotten by hand. Along the line at Cleveland there are automatic gauging devices consisting of steel prongs that reach into the workpiece and inspect every hole to make sure it has been drilled to precise depth. If the hole is not right, the gauge signals the next machine tool to stop work till the trouble is located, but while the checking is done *the line keeps moving*.

At the same time, the possibility of something going wrong is greatly reduced. With the workpiece smoothly passed along from one automated machine to another, it does not risk getting damaged by being knocked against the next piece.

By the same token, factory safety is enormously improved. Before the Cleveland plants were built, one of the jobs that had to be done by hand consisted of transferring hot, heavy coil springs from a coiling machine to a quench tank for cooling. The men who did it reached down, lifted the hot coil to chest height, turned around, and put it in a compression fixture, all within seconds. Around the plants the job was known as a "killer." No longer. Says D. S. Harder, the man who invented the word automation: "The reduction of accident rates, both in frequency and severity, on automated operations as opposed to those in nonautomated areas has been nothing short of amazing." In 1947, there were 10.30 disabling injuries per million man hours worked at Ford. In 1960, there were only 1.41 per million. Another factor with a safety angle is that jobs in automated plants are less monotonous.

Two Detroit consulting engineers, George H. Amber and Paul S. Amber, who double as faculty members at Wayne State University, are the creators of a very interesting chart that rationalizes the history, including the future, of automation. What Ford's Harder invented a word for is, actually, a new step in a historical series. The Ambers have used the word to cover the entire series from the first stone-age tool to tomorrow's science-fiction robot.

Their nomenclature consists of the letter A followed by a superscribed number. A_0 represents no automation at all and designates the orginal hand tools; A_1 represents powered tools and machines, and so on. A simplified version of the Amber & Amber automation chart follows.

Degree		Discussion	Examples
A_0	Hand tools and manual machines	Give mechanical advantages but do not replace man's energy or control.	Shovel, knife, pliers, axe, hammer, scissors, saw, block and tackle, handloom, typewriter.
A_1	Powered machines and tools	Replace man's energy with mechanical power (wind, water, steam, or electricity) but require man to position work and machine.	Electric hand drill, drill press, air hammer, power mower, spray gun, belt sander, portable floor polisher.
A_2	Single-cycle automatic and self-feed machines	Includes all single-cycle automatic machines. Operator must set up, load, initiate action, adjust, and unload.	Pipe-threading machine, radial drill, machine tools such as grinder, planer, mill, shaper, lathe.
A_3	Automatic cycle repeating	Includes all automatic machines. Loads, goes through sequence, unloads to next station. Not self-correcting. Obeys fixed or variable program such as cams, tapes, or cards. Includes transfer machines and Detroit automation.	Engine production lines, self-feeding press lines, automatic copying lathe, machines for making springs, bottles, hinges, chain, cartons, and doughnuts, and automatic packaging.
A_4	Self-measuring and adjusting	Measures and compares result to the desired size or position.	Automatic sizing grinders, color matching or blending, feed-

Degree		Discussion	Examples
	feedback	Two types: feedback control of surface of product, or positional control.	back control of machine-tool table, self-correcting tape-control machines.
A_5	Computer control, automatic cognition	Any process or problem that can be expressed as an equation can be computer-controlled. This includes automatic cognition, the awareness of variables in materials, process conditions, and work.	Turbine fuel control to vary fuel according to need of engine.
A_6	Limited self-programming	Machine sets up and tries subroutines based on general program. By remembering which actions were most effective, the machine learns by experience.	Utilization of inter-city telephone circuits, sophisticated elevator dispatching, neurological machines.
A_7	Relates cause from effects	Reasoning machine. Not only forecasts trends from incomplete data, but uses inductive reasoning, that is, synthesizes from facts.	Sales prediction, weather forecasting, lamp-failure anticipation, actuarial analysis.
A_8	Originality	Program designates only general form of desired action and eliminates clashes and disharmonies. Actual result is original work made to suit human taste.	Music-writing, fabric-designing, drug-formulating, poetry-writing machines. Machines to create original automatic machines.

Degree		Discussion	Examples
A_9	Commands others	This is the super-machine, capable of superior energy (A_1), dexterity (A_2), diligence (A_3), judgment (A_4), evaluation (A_5), learning (A_6), reasoning (A_7), and creativeness (A_8); would be able to dominate men.	The authors decline to cite examples of A_9 automation, leaving this to the science-fiction writers.

The first tool was a rock in the fist of Paleolithic man, and the first improvement on a tool was the handle Neolithic man tied to it. After that, man didn't do much except add refinements to the basic axe—better materials, better workmanship. Century after century he still grasped a handle attached to a blade or club and cut, drilled, pounded, gouged, or did whatever he needed to do. He had a few tricks—pulleys, levers, windlasses, and so on—to make his energy more effective, but it was still his own energy. Then came water power, then steam, and the revolution was here. With steam came power lathes, drill presses, milling machines, saws, and grinders. These power tools were followed within a century by the semiautomatic electric machine tools of the mass-production era, out of which have grown the fully automatic tools of the Ford engine plants.

The Ambers categorize automation another way, in four classes: military, industrial, office, and domestic. Military automation has created many miracles in its complicated realms of ranging, instrumentation, system engineering, and operations research. As long as the ultimate purpose of all of this remains unaccomplished, it is fair to say that military automation has been of great benefit in helping to develop the technology used by the other areas. Domestic automation, of course, makes life much easier with its dish- and clothes-washing machines, dryers, thermostat-controlled burners, not to mention automobiles, which are themselves becoming steadily more automatic.

But it is office and industrial automation that are effecting the real "second industrial revolution"—and more and better automation is just over the horizon. In 1960, United States manufacturers invested about $1½ billion in automation; by 1965, they were investing around $4 billion. (Other countries, notably Russia, are taking a similar path.) Such companies as Warner and Swazey, Cincinnati Milling, Bunker-Ramo, and other producers of automation equipment are steadily advancing the frontier. By 1970, half the machine tools in the United States will be fully automated. The aerospace industry has a process that is likely to spread to the auto industry—a clay mockup of a new model is photographed in three dimensions, translated into code for a punched tape, fed through automated die-making machines, template-making machines, and drafting machines. A still farther-out process now under development by IBM for General Motors involves a television picture tube. The machine is fed instructions about a part, and the part is reproduced on a screen on which a draftsman can make alterations by punching keys or using a beam-of-light pen. The machine then produces a microfilm copy that is enlarged into working drawings and a set of equations defining the part for drafting and milling machines.

It is a funny thing, but improvements in technology usually begin by scaring us to death. The steam locomotive, for example, stirred all kinds of alarm in Britain. The Duke of Wellington feared that it would facilitate a French invasion, and some Tory M.P.'s worried lest it lead to the corruption of young Etonians by enabling them to make quick trips to London.

Automation has raised specters ranging from mass unemployment to the supplanting of humanity by a race of metal monsters. Roughly, one man plus automation equals. forty men turning out engines a generation ago. It is easy to find more startling ratios. One glass-blowing plant is said to produce 90 percent of all the light bulbs used in the United States. The machinery is attended by just fourteen operators. One radio manufacturer has two workers plus automation turning out a thousand radios a day. Nor are the labor-saving feats of automation limited to manufacturing. Data processing is big business. The feats of computers make news. One at the California Institute of Technology took three hours to execute the eighty million calculations necessary to trace the evolution of the sun over its four-and-a-half-billion-year lifetime.

It has been said, with statistical accuracy, that automation is displacing between four and five thousand workers a day in shops and offices throughout the United States. There is a story of a visit to the Ford Cleveland plant by Walter Reuther, and a Ford official jestingly demanding of the U.A.W. president, "How are you going to collect any union dues from these machines, Walter?" To which Reuther replied, "How are you going to sell them any Fords?"

Machines certainly cannot buy their own products. Is automation threatening to ruin our market economy? Most experts think that more machines will mean more not fewer jobs. When the first Industrial Revolution hit England, the population of that little island country jumped from six or seven million people to thirty and forty million. More machines mean more production, more goods and services, more people and more jobs—a steady and rapid expansion of the whole economy.

There is widespread evidence to support the belief that contemporary automation is having the same effect. In the forty years since it put in automatic switching, American Telephone and Telegraph has increased its work force from three hundred and twenty thousand to seven hundred and sixty thousand, because automatic switching made possible an increase in telephones from ten million to seventy-five million.

Automation does indeed create a problem of radical job dislocation. It is taking away from a man a job he has learned, has developed skill in, has perhaps grown old in, and has acquired vested rights in, giving him in return one demanding a new start, new skills, loss of old fringe benefits, and an upset of his personal and family life.

In looking at contemporary automation—that is, automation over the remaining third of this century—it is important to observe that economics imposes certain brakes on the process. Computerized data processing is growing rapidly, and in some businesses has become a sort of religion or status rivalry. Yet if a computer that rents for $10,000 a month can only do the work of five $1,000-a-month junior executives, because that's all the work there is, then the computer is not worth renting.

An insufficient degree of standardization also deters the advance of total automation in many industries. Automobile assembly cannot be fully automated because all the cars are different. A green-and-white station wagon with push-button windows, radio speaker in the rear, and forty other optionals is followed off the line by a red convertible with windshield sprinklers, bucket seats, self-emptying ash trays, and the rest. Each car is put together individually from a dealer's specification sheet.

Even in a plant well suited to automation there are problems. Tools wear out, for example, without anybody noticing. This is what the Ambers call "down-time vulnerability." The more completely automatic a whole factory is, the more completely it has to shut down when any one part of it stops producing. There are many other barriers to full industrial automation, including reduced flexibility of operations, scheduling, and materials, and greater capital costs to start out with. Any manufacturer must balance these against the increased productive capacity, lower direct and indirect costs, and improved quality control.

But in the long run, as the American economy grows it will demand more and more automation. There will be more and more capital available in proportion to the number of workers, and the tendency for wages to rise in industries where skilled labor is in short supply will encourage management to use more automatic machinery.

It is safe to predict that the pace of technological advance will accelerate in time. The social changes wrought by automation will likewise accelerate, and increased production, increased leisure, and elimination of low-grade jobs in factory and office will proceed at a more and more rapid pace. Simultaneously, the power today pioneered by the N.S. *Savannah* will become available on an unimaginably massive scale through the development of fusion reactors. This brings us to the horizon of a society in which hardly any of the population will be needed to carry out the whole production process.

Hardly any? Why any at all? The truth is, as far as science can answer, science stands nonplussed. There is no demonstrable reason why some time in the next century the entire human race, say twenty or forty billion human beings, cannot be supported entirely by the labor of computers, the future offspring of our present material-handling devices and other automatic machinery. (Automation, it should be observed, is no stranger to the farm.)

The marriage of man and machine is irrevocable. It follows that a question of paramount importance is, who will be the dominant partner? It used to be said with confidence that machines could never get the upper hand because they could only do what men built them to do. This is no longer so positively asserted. IBM's projected models seem to be bringing us close to Mischa Richter's cartoon in *The New Yorker* in which a puzzled scientist reads the computer's tape and addresses his colleague: "It says, '*Cogito, ergo sum.*'"

Appendix A
Bridges

Long suspension spans

Site		Length in Feet of Suspended Span	Date Completed
Verrazano-Narrows	New York	4,260	1964
Golden Gate	San Francisco	4,200	1937
Mackinac Straits	Michigan	3,800	1957
George Washington	New York	3,500	1931
Lisbon-Tagus	Portugal	3,317	1966
Firth of Forth	Scotland	3,300	1964
Severn	England	3,240	1967
Bosporus	Turkey	3,100	1961
Tacoma Narrows	Puget Sound	2,800	1950

Long steel arches

Site		Length in Feet of Suspended Span	Date Completed
Bayonne	New Jersey	1,652	1931
Sydney Harbor	Australia	1,650	1932
Mersey River	Liverpool	1,082	1961
Birchenough	S. Rhodesia	1,080	1935
Saikai	Nagasaki, Japan	1,042	1955
Glen Canyon	Colorado River, Arizona	1,028	1959

213

	Site	Length in Feet of Suspended Span	Date Completed
Hell Gate	New York	977	1917
Rainbow	Niagara Falls, New York	950	1941
Clifton	Niagara Falls, New York	840	1898

Concrete arches

	Site		
Gladesville	Sydney, Australia	1,000	1964
Friendship	Brazil-Paraguay	952	1965

Cantilevers

	Site		
Quebec	Canada	1,800	1917
Firth of Forth	Scotland	1,700 (2 spans)	1889
New Orleans– Algiers	Louisiana	1,595	1958
Howrah	India	1,500	1943
Transbay	San Francisco	1,400	1936
Tappan Zee	Hudson River	1,212	1955

Longest covered bridge

	Site		
Hartland	New Brunswick, Canada	1,282	

Two great complex crossings

San Francisco–Oakland Bay Bridge: Two 2,300-foot suspension bridges, a large-bore rock tunnel, a 1,400-foot cantilever bridge, over six miles of trestle. Completed 1964.

Chesapeake Bay Bridge–Tunnel: Twelve miles of prestressed-concrete trestle, two high-level bridges (suspension and cantilever), multiple-span trusses and plate girders, and two midchannel tunnels with portals on artificial islands. Completed 1936.

Appendix B
Dams

Biggest (all earthfill)

	Location	Volume in Cubic Yards
Fort Peck	Montana	125,628,000
Oahe	South Dakota	91,000,000
San Luis	California	80,000,000
Oroville	California	78,000,000
Mangla	Pakistan	75,000,000
Garrison	South Dakota	66,500,000
Portage Mountain	Canada	60,000,000
Nurek	U.S.S.R.	58,000,000
Kiev	U.S.S.R.	58,000,000
Gorky	U.S.S.R.	58,000,000
Aswan	U.A.R.	53,000,000
Fort Randall	South Dakota	50,200,000
Kakhova	U.S.S.R.	46,000,000
Tsimlyansk-Kuibyshev	U.S.S.R.	44,000,000

Biggest concrete dam

Grand Coulee	Washington	10,500,000

Highest dams

	Location	Height in Feet	Type
Inguri	U.S.S.R.	990	Concrete
Nurek	U.S.S.R.	990	Earthfill
Grand Dixence	Switzerland	940	Concrete
Vaiont	Italy	860	Concrete
Mauvoisin	Switzerland	780	Concrete
Oroville	California	746	Earthfill
Bhakra	India	740	Concrete
Hoover	Colorado	730	Concrete
Glen Canyon	Arizona	710	Concrete
Luzzone	Switzerland	682	Concrete
Manicouagan No. 5	Canada	703	Concrete
Keban	Turkey	673	Earthfill
Dworshak	Idaho	670	Concrete
Dez	Iran	647	Concrete
Kurobe No. 4	Japan	630	Concrete
Portage Mountain	Canada	615	Earthfill
Shasta	California	602	Concrete

Biggest man-made lakes

	Location	Acre-Feet of Water, in Millions
Kariba	Rhodesia	149
Bratsk	Siberia, U.S.S.R.	145
Aswan	U.A.R.	127
Akosombo	Ghana	120
Manicouagan No. 5	Canada	115

Biggest hydroelectric plants

	Location	Maximum Kilowatt Capacity, in Millions
Krasnoyarsk	U.S.S.R.	6.0
Bratsk	U.S.S.R.	3.6

	Location	Minimum Kilowatt Capacity, in Millions
John Day	Oregon-Washington	2.7
Nurek	U.S.S.R.	2.7
Volgograd	U.S.S.R.	2.575
Portage Mountain	Canada	2.55
Kuibyshev	U.S.S.R.	2.3
Aswan	U.A.R.	2.1
Grand Coulee	U.S.	2.0

Longest dam

Hirakud, India, over Mahanadi River. 15.8 miles long, comprising two dikes, an earthfill dam, and a masonry dam.

Appendix C
Tunnels

Long mountain tunnels

	Location	Length in Miles
Simplon (rail)	Switzerland-Italy	12½
St. Gothard (rail)	Switzerland	9
Cascade (rail)	Colorado, U.S.	8
Frejus–Mont Cenis (rail)	France-Italy	7
Mont-Blanc (highway)	France-Italy	7

Longest water tunnel
Delaware Aqueduct, 105 miles, all in tunnel

Longest sewer tunnel
West Side Interceptor, Chicago, 20.6 miles

Longest aqueduct
California Aqueduct, 459 miles of tunnels and canals

Deepest tunnel below ground level
Simplon, 2,350 yards beneath summit of Monte Leone

Deepest below sea level
New York City Water Tunnel No. 1, 1,114 feet below the Hudson

First under-river tunnel
Thames Tunnel, Wapping to Rotherhithe, London; built by Marc Brunel, 1825–1842

First under-ocean tunnel
Kanmon Tunnel, Japan, connecting Honshu and Kyushu islands, 1936–1944

Appendix D
Structures

Tallest inhabited buildings

	Location	Floors	Height in Feet
* World Trade Center	New York	110	—
Empire State	New York	102	1,250
(including TV antenna)			1,472
John Hancock Center	Chicago	100	1,100
Chrysler	New York	77	1,046
60 Wall Tower	New York	67	950
Bank of Manhattan	New York	71	900
RCA, Rockefeller Center	New York	70	850
Chase-Manhattan	New York	60	813
Pan Am	New York	59	808
Woolworth	New York	60	746
City-Bank Farmers Trust	New York	57	741
Prudential Tower	Boston	52	750
Terminal Tower	Cleveland	52	708
Union Carbide	New York	52	707
Metropolitan Life	New York	50	700
Prudential	Chicago	41	601
(including TV antenna)			912

* Proposed

Tallest noninhabited (all TV antenna towers)

KXGO-TV	Fargo, North Dakota	2,063
KSLA-TV	Shreveport, Louisiana	1,898
WLRB-WTVM	Columbus, Georgia	1,749
WBIR	Knoxville, Tennessee	1,749
KFVS	Cape Girardeau, Missouri	1,676

Biggest Building (floor space)
The Pentagon, Arlington, Va., 6.5 million square feet

Biggest commercial building
Merchandise Mart, Chicago, 4,023,000 square feet

Biggest office building
Pan Am Building, New York, 2.4 million square feet of rentable space, 2.7 over-all

Appendix E
Experimental Communications Satellites

Name	Launch Date	Altitude of Initial Orbit in Statute Miles	Result Achieved
Score	December 18, 1958	115–914	Voice and telegraph communication for 13 days.
Courier I-A	August 18, 1960	—	Failed in launching.
Courier I-B	October 4, 1960	586–767	Voice, telegraph, telephoto, including voice to Puerto Rico.
Telstar I	July 10, 1962	593–3,503	TV, voice, telegraph, data, telephoto, transoceanic transmission.
Relay I	December 13, 1962	819–4,612	TV, voice, and so on, including transmissions to Europe, South America, and Japan.
Syncom I	February 13, 1963	21,268–22,974	Near circular orbit, but communications lost at outset.

Name	Launch Date	Altitude of Initial Orbit in Statute Miles	Result Achieved
Telstar II	May 7, 1963	604–6,713	Similar to Telstar I.
Syncom II	July 26, 1963	22,240–22,247	Orbit very nearly circular and synchronous.
Relay II	January 21, 1964	1,325–4,600	Similar to Relay I.
Syncom III	August 19, 1964	About 22,300	Close to perfect synchronous orbit; improved jet-control system.
Early Bird I	April 6, 1965	About 22,300	Very close to perfect synchronous orbit, first commercial transmissions.

Appendix F
Miscellaneous

Big ships

	Flag	Type	Tonnage
Nissho Maru	Japan	Tanker	·132,000
Universe Daphne	Liberia	Tanker	115,360
Universe Apollo	Liberia	Tanker	114,000
Manhattan	United States	Tanker	106,500
Mobil Brilliant	Britain	Tanker	97,000
Mobil Comet	Britain	Tanker	95,000
Universe Admiral	Liberia	Tanker	87,440
Universe Defiance	Liberia	Tanker	87,425
George Champion	Liberia	Tanker	87,416
Universe Commander	Liberia	Tanker	86,658
Esso Spain	Britain	Tanker	86,000
Harold H. Helm	Liberia	Tanker	85,592
Frisia	Liberia	Tanker	85,569
Universe Leader	Liberia	Tanker	85,515
Queen Elizabeth	Britain	Passenger	83,673
Queen Mary	Britain	Passenger	81,237

Big nuclear reactors (United States only)

Malibu Nuclear Plant, Los Angeles Department of Water and Power, at San Clemente, California, 463,000 net kilowatts (1967).

Connecticut Yankee Atomic Power Station, Haddam Neck, Connecticut, 463,000 net kilowatts (1967).

Nine Mile Point Plant, Oswego, New York, 500,000 net kilowatts (1968).

Bodega Bay Atomic Park, Bodega Head, California, 313,000 net
  kilowatts (1966).
Dresden Nuclear Power Station, Morris, Illinois, 208,000 net kilowatts (1959).

Big radio telescopes
Green Bank, West Virginia, diameter 300 feet.
Arecibo Ionospheric Observatory, Puerto Rico, 1,000-foot immo-
  bile mesh reflector.
Jodrell Bank, England, movable, diameter 250 feet.

Largest reflecting telescope
200-inch Hale Telescope, Mount Palomar, California.

World's highest arch
St. Louis Arch, 630 feet.

First domed stadium
Houston Astrodome, seating 45,000.

Appendix G
Top Engineering Projects
of the Sixties

Outstanding Civil Engineering Achievement Awards of the
American Society of Civil Engineers (awards instituted 1960)

1960: Winner:
St. Lawrence Power and Seaway Project

Other nominations:

Allegheny County Sewage Disposal System, Pennsylvania
(Award of Merit)
Oak Street Connector, New Haven, Connecticut
Torresdale Water Treatment Plant, Philadelphia, Pennsyl-
vania
Executive House, Chicago, Illinois
Scioto Downs, near Columbus, Ohio
Wilson Lock, Muscle Shoals, Alabama
Vandenberg Air Force Base, Los Angeles, California
Glen Canyon Bridge, Arizona
Priest Rapids Dam, Columbia River, Washington
Wichita-Valley Center Flood Control Project, Kansas

1961: Winner:
John F. Kennedy International Airport, New York

Other nominations:

Pan-American World Airways Terminal Building, Kennedy
Airport, New York
Chase Manhattan Bank, New York City, New York

Intelex Post Office Building, Providence, Rhode Island
Portage Lake Bridge, Houghton, Michigan
Dresden Nuclear Power Station, Chicago, Illinois
Hyperion Effluent Outfall, El Segundo, California
The Geysers Power Plant, Sonoma, California
Lloyd Center, Portland, Oregon
Grand Isle Sulphur Mine, Gulf of Mexico

1962: Winner:
Intercontinental Ballistic Missile Program

Other nominations:

Throgs Neck Bridge, New York
United Engineering Center, New York
Yankee Atomic Electric Plant, Rowe, Massachusetts
Niagara Power Plant, Niagara Falls, New York
District of Columbia Stadium, Washington, D.C.
Public Auditorium, Pittsburgh, Pennsylvania
Oahe Dam, near Pierre, South Dakota
Northwest Expressway, Chicago, Illinois
Bremerton Dry Dock, Bremerton, Washington
Underground Water System. Ada, Oklahoma

1963: Winner:
Ohio River Valley Clean Streams Program

Other nominations:

George Washington Bridge Expansion Project, New York
    (Award of Merit)
Whittier Narrows Water Reclamation Plant, Los Angeles
    County, California (Award of Merit)
University of Illinois Assembly Hall, Urbana, Illinois
Hardened Computer Center, Gloucester, Rhode Island
Trans-Sierra Highway Project, between Reno, Nevada,
    and Sacramento, California
Dulles International Airport, Chantilly, Virginia

1964: Winner:
Glen Canyon Dam, Page, Arizona

Other nominations:

Passenger-Cargo Pier, San Pedro, California
Marina City, Chicago, Illinois
IBM Building, Pittsburgh, Pennsylvania
Pan Am Building, New York City, New York
Taum Sauk Pumped Storage Hydroelectric Plant, near St.
    Louis, Missouri
San Francisco–Oakland Bay Bridge Reconstruction Project,
    California
TVA Water Control System

1965: Winner:
      Chesapeake Bay Bridge–Tunnel, Norfolk to Delmarva Pen-
      insula

      Award of Merit Winners:

      Verrazano-Narrows Bridge, New York
      Central District Filtration Plant, Chicago, Illinois
      Los Angeles County Flood Control District, California

Some leading foreign engineering projects of the sixties

    Africa: Kariba Hydroelectric Project
            New passenger railroad station at Cape Town
            Sewage works for Johannesburg
            Bulk ore storage and shipping installation at
               Port Elizabeth Harbor
            New ocean terminal at Durban Harbor
            Durban to Movi River Freeway

   Argentina: 60-story office-apartment building in Buenos Aires

   Australia: Melbourne Cultural Center
              Sydney Opera House
              Derwent River Bridge at Hobart
              Snowy Mountains Project

     Austria: Tyrol Bridge
              Aschach Power Plant on Danube

    Belgium: Charleroi Canal
              Floating docks, Antwerp

Germany: Nuclear Research Center, Julich
Bridge across the Fehmarn-Sund to Denmark
Underwater tunnel, Baltic-North Sea Canal, Rends-
burg
Hangar III, Frankfurt Airfield
Office building for Farbenfabriken Bayer, Lever-
kusen

India: Bhakra Dam
Rihand Dam
Nangal Fertilizer *cum* Heavy Water Plant
Bokaro Steel Project
Talcher Thermal Power Station

Iran: Dez Dam

Japan: Tokyo-Nagoya-Kobe Expressway
Expressway development in Tokyo metropolitan
area
Kurobe No. 4 dam project
Okutadami Hydroelectric Project
Wakato Bridge
Osaka Freeway System
Osaka Rapid Transit Plan
Tokyo Urban Transit System

New Zealand: Geothermal power development at Waitaki
Direct current cable across Cook Strait

Norway: Tokke Hydroelectric Project
Tromso Bridge

Spain: Guadarrama Tunnel

Sweden: Underground shelters

Appendix H
Future Wonders

EVERYBODY KNOWS about the space stations, satellites, moon shots, Mars shots, Jupiter shots, far-out shots. Below are some earth-bound engineering prospects for the next few years:

The fusion reactor. The breakthrough on this, when it comes, will be the biggest development in power history, opening unlimited possibilities in many directions.

Nuclear excavation. More immediately, atomic blasting offers a promising technique for cutting through major geographical and topographical barriers, such as the Central American isthmus. Nuclear excavating will be done with special charges fired in strings, buried in such a way as to produce the desired cratering and at the same time causing the fallback of earth to rebury the radiation.

The megastructure. An architect's nickname for the future multiple-use high-rise building, hundreds of floors of offices, shops, apartments, schools, recreation facilities—the vertical suburb which may be the most conspicuous feature of the next generation's cities.

Supercrossings. The multiple-dome caisson, cheap high-strength steel alloys, and other new developments make very long crossings over deep water highly feasible. The Chesapeake Bay Bridge points the way to bridge-trestle and bridge-tunnel developments inconceivable a few years ago. Ocean tunnels are likely, in the wake of tunnels under the English Channel, the Straits of Gilbraltar, the Bosporus, Bering Strait, and many others.

Ocean dams. With the main rivers of the world rapidly turning into complete ladders of dams and locks, it is time to harness the ocean tides. French engineers have made an important breakthrough at Saint Malo, harnessing the outflow as well as the inflow of the Rance estuary tides. Harnessed both ways, many narrow bays in North America and Europe have big power potential.

Major water diversion. The Australian Snowy Mountains scheme, by which mountain waters are to be diverted with the aid of nine major dams and many smaller ones, 100 miles of large-bore tunnels, and 80 miles of aqueducts, for irrigation and power has been under construction since 1949. Among similar projects for the not distant future is a rather easy one for turning around the waters that flow into James Bay and replenishing the Great Lakes with them.

Supertunnels. Systems engineer Larry Edwards' proposal for a 500-mph pneumatic tube for the much-discussed Northeast Transit scheme is the most intriguing of many involving tunnels hundreds of miles long. The technical basis for all of these is the boring machine, now capable of grinding through many kinds of rock and on the verge of replacing traditional tunneling methods.

Index